PRAEGER INTRODUCTORY GEOGRAPHIES

Spain

Praeger Introductory Geographies

FRANCE
E. Estyn Evans

ITALY
J. P. Cole

HUMAN GEOGRAPHY
Emrys Jones

SPAIN
An Introductory Geography

by

W. B. FISHER

and

H. BOWEN-JONES

FREDERICK A. PRAEGER, *Publishers*

New York · Washington

BOOKS THAT MATTER

Published in the United States of America
in 1966 by Frederick A. Praeger, Inc., Publishers
111 Fourth Avenue, New York, N.Y. 10003

The original edition of this book
was published in 1958
by Chatto & Windus, London

Library of Congress Catalog Card Number: 66-17362

Printed in the United States of America

PREFACE

IT is hoped in this study to make accessible to high school, college, and university students, as well as to readers generally, some background information on present-day Spain. Material on the physical and human geography of Spain is remarkably scattered; and our hope is that the present small volume will bring together, however cursorily, a number of basic elements relating to Spain which at present can be found only by collation from several separate sources.

One reason for the relative disinterest in Spain is perhaps the language barrier: in the future, as the value and interest of Spanish come to be even more appreciated in the United States, this will decline. Another is certainly the lack of information from Spain itself. For certain regions, knowledge is incomplete—one can offer only approximations or theories: as, for example, concerning aspects of structure, since a full geological investigation is yet to be made; or as regards climatic data, owing to the scanty 'cover' of meteorological reporting stations.

One or two explanations are perhaps due. We have followed the now well-known and accepted pattern of presenting our topic under three heads: the physical basis, human and economic background, and regional studies. Inclusion of cultural, historical and social questions is, we feel, justified by the nature of conditions within Spain. It is impossible fully to comprehend the geography of the country without some reference to history. Equally, no account of Spanish historical evolution could safely ignore the sustained influence of environment on human development. Our survey has drawn on a number of classical studies in Spanish and French, supplemented in some instances by personal investigation in the field.

Use of place-names is not wholly consistent: we have judged it pedantic to employ Andalucia, Catalunya, Duero, Navarra, Sevilla and Tajo for the well-known anglicised forms, but otherwise names are as written in Spanish, with the accent indicating a stress in speech, if this does not fall on the penultimate vowel, as is usual. It has not always been possible or desirable to limit the discussion (particularly in the physical

v

section) to the frontiers of Spain; hence 'Iberia' has been used to indicate the peninsula as a whole.

Our grateful thanks are due to Mr. E. Craig, Vice-Consul of Spain at Newcastle-on-Tyne, for most helpful information on contemporary conditions; and the kindness of the Cultural Section, Spanish Embassy, London; the Spanish Tourist Bureau, London; and the British Thomson-Houston Co. Ltd., for the use of photographs. One of us is glad to acknowledge, as an element in present interest in Spain, the teaching of Professor E. Sarmiento; and the other, great help and kindness received from the family of the late Juan Dantín Cereceda.

W.B.F.
H.B-J.

Durham
February 1958

PUBLISHER'S NOTE

Some changes have been made in this American edition. Population figures for cities of 100,000 and over are based mainly on the censuses of 1963; for smaller cities, on the national census of 1960. More recent production figures are derived from issues of the United Nations *Statistical Yearbook*.

CONTENTS

vii

Part III Regional Geography

LIST OF PLATES

(*Following Page 216*)

LIST OF MAPS

Spain

Chapter 1

INTRODUCTORY

FOR many centuries Spain lay at the western limit of the known world. To early Phoenician and Greek travellers, its almost sheer coastline, mountainous interior and climatic extremes made it forbidding and unrewarding of access—the Dark Continent of the early Classical age. Its name, from the Semitic *Span*, means 'hidden'.

In later times the surprising variety within the country seemed an outstanding feature: the Romans hence referred to it as 'The Spains'—an appraisal which later rulers confirmed. Down to Alfonso XIII the monarch took the title 'King of the Spains'.

Nowadays, the geographer with an eclectic view of lands and peoples might be tempted to regard the Iberian peninsula as a mirror-image of Asia Minor. In the two regions there is the same physical pattern of daunting topography, unexpectedly varied and severe climates, and a wide range in ways of life. Both have been the centres of large empires, now in eclipse; and both have remained partly secluded from the main currents of European affairs, with interests away from Europe; both have impinged politically for limited periods but with profound effect, on the course of history in Europe, as centres of invasion outwards, and as zones of weakness that have attracted predatory neighbours. Finally, both include in their territory sea straits that are regarded as vital spheres of influence by more northerly powers.

Just as there is some doubt as to where in south-east Europe lies the frontier with Asia, so one encounters the cliché that Africa begins at the Pyrenees. Like so many clichés, it is an overstatement, some would say misleading, but it also contains a modicum of truth. The physical continuation of the Betic

chains into North Africa is more clearly demonstrable than
their prolongation into Europe, however much geologists dis-
agree over precise details. Also, the Saharan origin of certain
air-masses that affect much of Spain cannot be disputed. Moreover, the Arab interlude in Spain, with its consequent effect
on Spanish culture, reinforces from the side of human geography the affinities to Africa. What cannot be gainsaid is the
partial relationship in environment between Spain and North
Africa. Whether in consequence one can legitimately regard
the Atlas Mountains as the frontier of Europe, or the Pyrenees
as the boundary of Africa is in one sense beside the point,
which is that there are undeniable elements common to both
Spain and North Africa. This matter will be referred to again
in subsequent pages.

With its 196,000 square miles of territory, Spain ranks after
Russia and France as the third European country in size. The
average height of the Iberian peninsula is just under 2200 ft.—
exceeded in Europe only by Switzerland. This, together with
its extreme south-westerly position, and the fact that its highest
mountain ranges lie nearest to the junctions with other land-
masses, makes for isolation. The south-westerly situation is not
always fully appreciated. Madrid, roughly in the centre of the
country, lies farther south than Naples and Istanbul, farther
west than Bristol or Liverpool. Gibraltar is in approximately
the same latitude as Malta and Aleppo.

There are no clear and obviously practicable lowland routes
across the peninsula: no Gap of Carcassonne, or Rhône valley.
Even atmospheric depressions tend to pass otherwise than
across the centre of the Meseta. If France and Germany are
classic routeways (*durchgangsländer*), Spain is, so to speak, one
of Nature's termini.

In France, one can point to symmetry, balance and regularity. Iberia has a fairly simple, squarish shape, but there the
matter ends. Strabo regarded the country as a mass of opposing
factors; contradiction and contrast are the words used by
Allison Peers to describe Spain: austerity and fecundity are the
descriptions most used by Sorre in his study of Spanish geography. It is now theoretically possible to travel in the same

single railway coach from London to Basra or Teheran: but not from Paris to Madrid.

Westerly position has however conferred on Spain a considerable advantage. The country is well placed for Atlantic travel, and contact with the Americas. With our own British relationships in northern America, we are sometimes inclined to overlook the extent of past, and present, Spanish influence in the New World. This, despite vicissitudes, is still recognised by many Latin Americans as valuable and to be developed—'the dual cultural past of Spanish and indigenous cultures is the very basis of our existence', writes L. Zea, a native of Mexico. Moreover, Spanish relations with South America have made Spanish the second or third most widespread language in the world, after English and Russian.

Two further aspects of this contact are political. The new interest, and even respect, of the United States for Spain as a possible ally; and the suggestions from South America of a pan-Latin grouping on a Spanish linguistic and cultural basis may well become more significant in the future. Spain is far from being solely a 'Mediterranean' power.

Part I

THE PHYSICAL BASIS

Chapter 2

STRUCTURE AND RELIEF

UNLIKE its near neighbours France and Italy, where geological formation is relatively simple, and the observer can discern a straightforward relationship between topography and rock structure, Spain presents conditions of remarkable complexity. There is no pattern of river basins composed of less resistant sedimentary rocks, and uplands of older, harder strata, as in France; or no single mountain chain controlling the entire disposition of the country, as in Italy. Instead, Spain shows a bewildering variety of physical conditions and rock types; and can best be regarded as a patchwork of widely differing elements. Mountain massifs extend in a most irregular pattern. Certain sections can be of relatively great age, whilst other nearby ranges, or even adjoining parts of the same mass, are of much later origin. There are extensive plateaux, some of which are granitic, like those of the northern Highlands of Scotland; and others, which though of equal height, are composed of much younger and softer limestones, sandstones and chalk, like the rocks of East Anglia. Even the lowlands are by no means uniform—some have been produced by erosion and hence have a generally sinuous trend, a V-shaped profile, and rounded slopes; whilst other lowlands are of tectonic origin—i.e. they have been formed by faulting and dislocation of the underlying strata, and in consequence have a flat floor, and abrupt, steep sides.

The dominating structural element in Spain is the Meseta:

a rigid mass, or block, of relatively old and resistant rocks that were heavily folded and subjected to great heat and pressure in Hercynian times (*c.* 220 million years ago). Much of the original rock has in consequence been metamorphosed into schist, gneiss and granite, and many traces of the original structure lost; but it would seem that the Meseta formed part of a larger mass, since comparable fragments (on a smaller scale) occur in North Africa, southern France and Corsica. It has also been suggested that traces exist in Spain of an even earlier phase of earth movement (the Caledonid, which produced the ranges of northern Scotland and Scandinavia)—but evidence on this point is very doubtful.

Following the Hercynian period of disturbance and mountain-building, there was a prolonged era of denudation, during which sediments eroded from the land surface accumulated in deep seas adjacent to the Meseta. At times, the seas transgressed over parts of the Meseta, leaving sedimentary deposits, some of which now remain as sandstones and limestones. In other parts, further metamorphism transformed these deposits into schist and slate.

Towards the end of the Mesozoic period (*c.* 70 million years ago) a renewed series of earth movements, originating generally from the south and directed towards the north and west, culminated in the last great phase of mountain building —the Alpine orogeny. The more pliable sedimentary rocks fringing the Meseta were rucked up into fold structures, whilst the Meseta itself was tilted and buckled, and its northern, eastern and southern edges deformed to varying degrees. Along the edge where pressure was greatest (i.e. on the southeast) the Meseta was uptilted to form the Sierra Morena ranges; and similar uptilting on a slightly smaller scale affected the northern and eastern margins.

Further dislocation, reduced but not damped out entirely by the resistant basal layers of the Hercynian block, gave rise to wrinkling of the surface layers within the Meseta itself, producing the upland chains of central Spain. In the north, the Pyrenees, formed of newly-laid down sediments, and broadly comparable in age and structure with the Alps, came

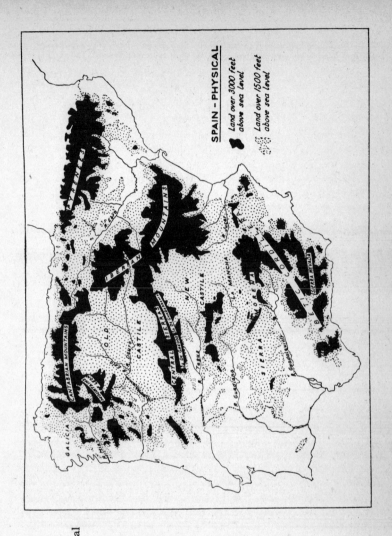

1 Spain, Physical

into existence at this time. On the south, the Sierra Nevada, another fold-structure clearly related to the Atlas chains of North Africa, was another product of the great Alpine orogeny, which, beginning at the end of the Mesozoic period, reached its culmination during the Cainozoic or Tertiary geological era.

Another feature of this period was the development of great faults, or fracture-lines, particularly in the west. One extensive system came into existence approximately at the line of the present-day coast, with downthrow on the seaward side, thus producing the sheer, abrupt coastline now characteristic of many parts of the north and west. An inland continuation of a fault can be traced due south from Oporto through Abrantes as far south as Cape St. Vincent.

The final phase in the geological history of Spain has been one of irregular oscillation, with changes in the relative level of land and sea. Considerable erosion of the land surface has taken place, reducing many of the higher and craggier uplands to rounded massifs, and spreading the eroded material in extensive layers over lowland areas. At times, the sea has invaded the land; and great lakes—both salt and fresh—have formed on the lower-lying areas of the Meseta, leaving widespread deposits of mud, sand and shingle. Many old strand-lines and irregular terraces also indicate the wide variation in relative level of land and sea. Also, valleys worn into the rock-surface have been 'drowned' by subsidence or flooding at their seaward end, producing the 'ria' formation—a winding arm of the sea extending far inland. This is well exemplified in north-west Spain: e.g. at Vigo, where the present-day ria is over 15 miles long.

Broadly speaking, Spain can be said to comprise two main zones of contrasting surface deposits. In the west, older and more resistant crystalline rocks predominate (granites, schists and quartzites), producing a topography of undulating highland massifs, with intervening level stretches (peneplanes). In the centre and east, limestones of later formation are the dominant rock type; and these weather into a karstic tableland (*paramo*), that rises by steep slopes (*cuestas*) from level valleys floored by sands and clays. The valleys can be of varied char-

acter—open and basin-like, or deep and tortuous, with precipitous sides.

The Northern Highland Zone. This may be said to comprise the
Pyrenees and their westward extension, the Cantabrian
mountains. The Pyrenees themselves extend in a remarkably
uniform and relatively unbroken pattern from the Mediterranean coastlands to the southern shores of the Bay of Biscay,
reaching a maximum height of 11,169 ft. (Pic d'Aneto) and
remaining well above 5000 ft. over most of their length. The
fold-structures are not symmetrical, but appear to be as it were
'pushed over' towards the north; so that there is in general an
abrupt drop from an unbroken crest-line on the northern
(French) side, and a more gradual fall by steps (or terraces)
towards the Ebro (Spanish) side.

In topography the Pyrenees much resemble the Alps, with
even a few glaciers, which, however, are small. But large-scale
cirques and deep ice-cut valleys indicate that during the
Quaternary Ice Age snowfields covered much of the Pyrenees
area. Scenically, and hence touristically, the French side is
more attractive than the southern (Ebro) slopes. Moreover,
the continuity and regularity of the high ridges contrasts
strongly with conditions in the Alps, which though possessing
higher individual massifs, are much more broken up by valleys.
This means that major road and rail routes must pass round
the eastern and western ends of the Pyrenees, which hence
remain very sparsely peopled and isolated. It is because of
these conditions that the political anachronism of Andorra has
been able to survive as a semi-independent territorial unit.

In the extreme west the Pyrenees become more rounded, and
drop in average height to under 4000 ft., passing ultimately
into a territory of somewhat irregular uplands broken by
numerous deep and narrow valleys. This is the Basque
country; and the differences in topography as compared with
the Pyrenees can be ascribed mainly to a more extensive occurrence of softer rocks, with in consequence a greater degree of

erosion. Structurally the Basque territory is merely a continuation of the Pyrenees—i.e. there is a similar pattern of ranks of folded rock strata.

Farther west still, in the region behind Bilbao, Santander and Oviedo, the mountains again become extensive and imposing, with the development of a few relatively unbroken ridges that extend over 80–100 miles, and reach an average height of 5000–6000 ft., with several summits 2000 ft. higher still. These are the Cantabrian Mountains—almost as impressive in size and altitude as the Pyrenees, and equally a barrier to movement north and south. On their northern (seaward) side, the descent to the Biscayan coast is extremely steep, with only a tiny coastal plain that is often broken by stretches where hills drop directly into the sea. On the south side, the drop is less abrupt. Towards the north-west corner of Spain, relief again becomes somewhat more subdued, and the whole area, known as Galicia, is best described as a low plateau dropping gradually towards the north and west.

Structurally, Galicia exhibits marked individuality. The massive east–west running folds characteristic of the Pyrenees and Cantabrian massifs disappear: instead, the main physical features have been produced by faulting and tilting, with fault-lines running in a north–south or north-east–south-west direction. Rock type too is strikingly different. Whereas the Pyrenees, Basque hills and Cantabrians are composed mostly of limestone and some sandstones (of Tertiary age in the east, and Carboniferous age in the west), schists, slate and granite predominate in Galicia. As a result, there is a distinctive landscape of more rounded hills, with granite 'tors' somewhat reminiscent of Cornwall and Devon, and patches of lowland close to the sea. The change from lowland to upland is sometimes very sudden, hence waterfalls are characteristic of many Galician rivers.

The Central Meseta. By far the largest proportion of Spain is occupied by the Meseta, which, however, is far from being a uniform mass. It is best regarded as comprising two enormous table-lands, or upland basins, which are separated by a

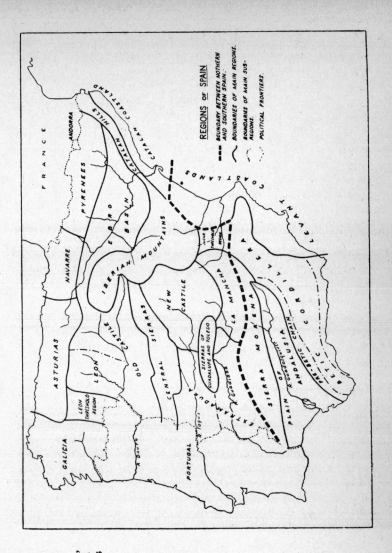

2 Spain, Natural Regions

diagonally-running fold mountain series: the Central Sierras, which extend irregularly from west-south-west to east-north-east across the middle of the Meseta. These Sierras have different names—e.g. Sierra de Guadalupe, Montes de Toledo, Sierra de Guadarrama; and it is thought that this entire highland mass, which consists partly of folds, and partly of fault-structures, came into existence during early Tertiary times (Eocene–Miocene), and is thus related structurally to the Pyrenees and Sierra Nevada.

The central Sierras rise to about 9000 ft., and consist mainly of granites and schists, which weather into an imposing series of rounded summits and irregular valleys of varying kinds. On the whole, the Sierras present a rather forbidding landscape of gaunt rock shoulders, and bare granite outcrops; and the height of the fold-structures, together with the lack of easy crossing-points, make them a considerable obstacle to communications across the Meseta.

Between the Central Sierras on the south, the Portuguese highlands to the west, and the Cantabrian mountains on the north, lies the northern of the two table-lands that make up most of the Meseta. This extends for about 150 miles from north to south, and 100 miles east to west, and comprises the historical region of León and Old Castile. Most of the floor of the basin lies at an average altitude of 2700 ft. above sea-level in the east, and slopes gradually down to about 2200 ft. at the Portuguese frontier. The granitic basement series are largely covered by Tertiary sandstones, limestones, marls and clays, and the granite appears only as irregular series of low ridges round the margins. Over most of the basin the prevailing impression is that of flatness—the rivers are cut fairly deeply into the horizontal strata, leaving extensive residual table-lands of chalk or limestone. In other parts, where softer rocks occur, wide valleys with flat floors have been eroded out. Uniform weathering of a regular and horizontal rock series has produced what to the ordinary observer seems an extremely monotonous landscape—an impression which is heightened by the scantiness of the vegetation cover. To the physical geographer, however, Old Castile has especial interest in possessing 'one of the most perfect erosion-surfaces in the world' (Birot).

Towards the eastern and northern margins, erosive agents have been even more active. Material removed from the encircling mountain rim has been deposited in extensive sheets over the plateau-surface; and deposits range from coarse pebbles near the mountain foot to fine alluvium in the more distant river valleys.

The southern table-land of the Meseta, covering about 45,000 square miles, is nearly three times larger than its northern counterpart: and, together, the two basins form the largest and most imposing plateau surface in Europe. Altitude in the south is however less, averaging only 1700–2000 ft.; and again there is a slight tilt to the west—the lowest parts therefore occurring in Extramadura and along the Portuguese frontier. In the eastern districts (New Castile) there is a cover of Tertiary sediments—clays, sands and limestones—and differences of hardness produce minor variations in topography. Towards the west, however, the older and more resistant basement rocks are frequently exposed, and have been worn into a succession of valleys and irregular upland ridges that in the main run from west to east (e.g. the Montes de Toledo, and Sierra da S. Pedro). Patches of less resistant younger rocks are not entirely absent, hence the topography can range from rocky uplands that reach as much as 4500 ft. (e.g. the Sierra de Guadalupe) to the open monotonous plain of La Mancha, or the narrow defiles of the upper Guadiana river, which are too steep and narrow for a major road.

In the extreme south, as a boundary zone to the whole area, occurs the Sierra Morena, which is merely the uptilted and buckled edge of the Meseta. Intense pressure from the south, occurring in irregular phases at the time of the formation of the Pyrenees and Alps, thrust newer sediments against the southern border of the Meseta, which in this particular region had a sedimentary rock layer covering the granite basement. Extensive dislocation has resulted, the chief effect being the formation of horsts—i.e. detached blocks lifted above the general level. Thus the Sierra Morena is not a true fold-structure, but a series of isolated upland masses separated by areas of lower relief, and dropping much more steeply towards the south, where it overlooks the low-lying Plain of Andalusia. Rise of volcanic magma and other deposits along the fault-lines and other zones of weakness has also led firstly to minor variations in surface topography, and secondly, to extensive mineralisation. In the Sierra Morena area occur important deposits of copper, lead, mercury and wolfram.

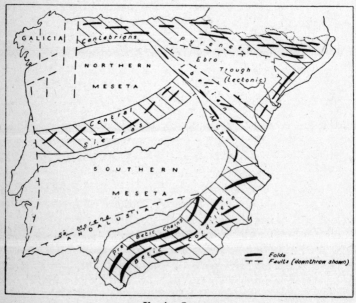

3 Iberia, Structure

The Iberian Mountains. From Burgos south-eastward as far as the Mediterranean coast near Valencia there extends an irregular upland mass known as the Iberian or Celtiberian mountains. This system continues directly from the central Cantabrian mountains, thus forming the eastern rim of the basin of Old Castile, and separating this basin from the Ebro trough farther east. Southwards, the Iberian mountains join on to the Central Sierras of the Meseta, and farther south still, again form an eastward boundary for the basin of New Castile.

The entire mountain mass is made up of a series of fold structures, mainly of Tertiary age (Oligocene–Pliocene), and heavily eroded at a subsequent period, so that older Palaeozoic and Mesozoic rocks and Hercynian fold-structures are sometimes exposed. The sequence of longitudinal fold-ridges, separated by extensive plateau zones and occasional deep valleys, recalls in some ways the Appalachian mountains of eastern North America.

The Ebro Basin. This area, more or less triangular in shape, must originally have come into existence as a relatively undisturbed zone between three systems of folds—the Pyrenees on the north, the Iberian mountains to the west and south, and the Mediterranean coastal ranges on the east. Rock series lie for the most part horizontally, but have been differentially eroded, so that many minor differences in landscape occur. The more resistant sandstones and limestones stand out as flat-topped plateaux; whilst a labyrinth of steep narrow valleys have been cut by small rivers into the softer clays and marls. The valleys of the larger rivers are on the other hand extremely broad, with suites of very well-developed terraces. Altogether, the succession of flat-topped plateaux or isolated buttes, dropping in steps to a riverine plain, produces a landscape markedly different from that of the fold-mountains to the north and west: monotony and regularity are the chief features, with (in areas where limestone predominates) extreme scantiness of surface water, and a general karstic topography.

The Ebro basin is not however one simple lowland triangle; there is an upper portion lying at a somewhat higher level—1100 ft., as compared with 750 ft. average altitude in the lower part. This higher section covers about one-fifth of the total area of the Ebro trough, and is separated from the remainder by two outlying spurs of high ground. One extends southwards from the main mass of the Pyrenees, the other continues north-eastwards from the Iberian mountains. Where the two almost meet, near Tudela, the Ebro valley is very greatly constricted.

Thus, despite its generally lowland character, the Ebro basin does not offer particularly good facilities for easy movement, and it is on the whole an obstacle rather than an aid to the development of through routes into eastern, northern and central Spain. It isolates adjacent areas rather than links them together.

The Barrier Ranges of the East and South—(*a*) *The Catalonian Ranges*. The seaward end of the Ebro basin is almost entirely closed by a series of ridges running parallel to the coast; and the river itself is deflected southwards, ultimately breaking through the ridges by an extremely narrow and deep gorge. Emerging from this coastal upland zone, the Ebro finally enters the Mediterranean well to the south-west of its middle and upper course through an imposing delta.

Two main ridges can be discerned—the first actually on the coast, running north-eastwards and south-westwards of Barcelona. This reaches a maximum height of 1500–1700 ft., and produces a picturesque coastline of high cliffs and sheltered sandy coves. Predominance of granite enhances the structural —if not climatic—similarity to the coasts of Devon and Cornwall.

Behind this coastal ridge occur first a lowland strip about 12 miles wide, and then the second or interior ridge, which is distinctly more imposing, reaching 5000 ft. in the extreme north-east. Whilst the coastal sierra is mainly of granite with some limestone and sandstone, the interior sierra is composed chiefly of Jurassic limestone, with however some granitic intrusions, and, in the north-east, basaltic cones and lava flows. Farther still, towards the interior, the sierra drops more gradually by a series of scarps and alluvial hollows to the main Ebro trough.

(*b*) *The Andalusian Highlands, or Betic Cordillera*. This series of uplands, extending for over 350 miles, is best regarded as an irregular series of mountain ridges separated by upland basins, and broken by deep troughs or passes. One of the largest mountain units is the Sierra Nevada, and in some texts the name is applied to the whole of the Betic Cordillera between Gibraltar and Alicante. More correctly, however, the term Sierra Nevada should be restricted to one particular massif occurring between Granada and Almeria—i.e. the central portion only of the Andalusian Highlands.

Structurally, the Andalusian massifs are extremely complex. There has been a considerable degree of crustal disturbance, producing more especially in the south a series of longitudinal folds that can be traced in an arc from Gibraltar north-eastwards as far as the Balearic Islands. Besides this, nappes have been produced—i.e. the intensity of earth movement has forced one rock series above another, with impaction of several original layers. Consequently, towards the north-west side of the Andalusian Highlands, a fragmented structural pattern occurs, with portions of one rock series as it were squeezed out of the normal position and pushed over towards the north-west. The extent of this displacement is a matter of some controversy. Various explanations are put forward as to the extent to which one rock formation over-rode another, and the precise distance is not so far clearly established.

The Betic Cordillera contains the highest summit in Spain (the crest of the Sierra Nevada, 11,420 ft.); but, in strong contrast to the Pyrenees, is broken firstly by a well-marked central trough, which divides the whole range into two. Secondly, north–south running rifts produce relatively broad transverse valleys that afford direct access from north to south. In this way, the entire Betic Cordillera is broken into a series of detached uplands with intervening valleys or plateaux. Consequently, despite its greater maximum height, and roughly equivalent width, the system is far less of a barrier to north–south communications as compared with the Pyrenees.

Rock type varies considerably from limestones and sandstones to slate, schist and igneous intrusions: and the resulting differences in resistance to erosion have produced a very varied landscape. Lowland pockets, narrow coastal plains, plateaux, jagged peaks and deep ravines alternate frequently within a short distance. Consequently, though formed approximately at the same geological period as the Pyrenees and by the same process of compression of pliable rock series against harder ancient blocks, the Betic Cordillera shows important differences as compared with its northern counterpart.

The Plain of Andalusia. This is a triangular-shaped area lying between the Betic Cordillera and the Central Meseta, and forms the only important lowland area in Spain that communicates directly with the sea—in other words, the only extensive lowland corridor giving easy access to the interior. The plain is a simple rift structure: i.e. produced by downthrow along faults lying to the north and to the south.

At one time the lowland was drowned by the sea, and there is hence a layer of Tertiary marine deposits covering most of the valley floor. As these deposits consist mostly of clays, erosion by the river Guadalquivir and its tributaries has been very active, and the surface is gently undulating, with the rivers lying in broad shallow valleys, in the sides of which appear numerous terraces. Towards the east, away from the sea, as the general level of the plain rises, the rivers become more incised in their beds, and differences in topography are somewhat more marked. But in the west, downstream of Seville, the land is extremely flat, and drops less than 50 ft. in 50 miles. Here occurs a landscape not unlike that of the Mesopotamian plain: the main river divides into many distributaries which wander over a marshy plain (*Las Marismas*), whilst towards the higher ground on either side extensive arid sandy areas give an impression of semi-desert.

DRAINAGE

We may first note certain features common to most Spanish rivers. Volume, in relation to the size of the territory drained, is small; flow is rapid, even torrential, but highly variable, both from day to day and seasonally. Because of the swift flow, the river beds tend to be strongly V-shaped, deeply incised and with an irregular profile, i.e. usually broken by cascades or rapids. All this is summed up in the saying that Spanish rivers have 'a long name, a narrow channel, and little water'. We may usefully be reminded that cañon is a Spanish word: the river valleys of Spain have special characteristics—often leaving no space for routes, and a hindrance to movement rather than an encouragement.

So much for the general similarities. In view of the irregular topography and widely varying incidence of rainfall, it is also the case that the drainage and flow-patterns show corresponding variations in type. There are, first, the long well-developed rivers with an extensive catchment area—such as the Ebro, Guadalquivir, Douro, Tagus and Guadiana (the last three flowing for the shorter part of their course through Portugal). Secondly, there are the short but very swift streams descending abruptly from the northern coastal ranges, or outer edge of the Meseta: these in general carry much water. Finally, there are a number of areas of aretic (i.e. inland) or indeterminate drainage—with streams that cannot break through encircling upland ranges, and hence end in a marsh, or salt pan, or even seep underground.

Chapter 3

CLIMATE

Variation in Climatic Conditions. Perhaps nowhere else in Europe, with the possible exception of Italy, is such a wide variation of climate to be found as in Spain. On the west, temperate conditions characteristic of north-west Europe extend farther south than anywhere else on the seaboard of the Atlantic; on the east, the semi-arid regions associated with south-west Asia and North Africa extends farthest north.

Though some districts of north-west Spain have between 60 and 70 ins. of rainfall annually (equivalent to that of parts of the English Lake District), the most pronounced Spanish climatic feature is however aridity—especially surprising, at first sight, in a region almost entirely surrounded by large expanses of sea. Some two-thirds of Spain experience a deficient rainfall in four months out of every twelve, i.e. defined as insufficient rainfall for normal plant growth, regard being paid to prevailing temperatures. Using this same standard of comparison, it is interesting to note that hardly any of France comes into this category, only the extreme southern tip of Italy, and less than one-quarter of Greece and European Turkey. Put somewhat more simply, about 65% of Spain has a total annual rainfall of 20 ins. or less, and about 8% has less than 15 ins.

Another fact, remarkable in view of the traditional idea of Spain as a region with a classic 'Mediterranean' type of climate (i.e. with a winter maximum of rainfall), is that in many districts of Spain rainfall over the summer half-year (March–September) exceeds that of the winter six months.

Here are important contrasts; and the chief explanation for them is the great height and extent of the Iberian peninsula, which has the effect cf generating its own special weather conditions. Oceanic influences from the Atlantic and Mediterranean are restricted to narrow coastal strips, and in the interior of the land-mass much local modification of rainfall and temperature can occur.

A second, somewhat less important influencing factor—though far from being negligible—is the nearness of North Africa. Separated from the hot, arid steppes of Algeria and Morocco only by a narrow arm of the Mediterranean, much of Spain as far north as the Ebro valley can from time to time be affected by weather phenomena that have originated in or near the Sahara Desert. As regards climate and weather, the zone of contact between Spain and North Africa is almost as extensive as that between Spain and Europe—a matter which is of significance not only as regards climate, but in other ways as well.

Pressure Conditions. Many readers will be familiar with the general factors affecting atmospheric pressure in Mediterranean countries. The seasonal migration of pressure-zones brings regions situated round about 40° N. latitude into an area of high pressure in summer, and into one of low pressure in winter. This situation is in broad outline true for the whole of the Iberian peninsula. The southward swing during winter of an extensive low-pressure belt normally over Britain and France can often affect Spain, and when this occurs, systems of depressions pass eastwards over the peninsula from the Atlantic towards the Mediterranean.

But also for prolonged periods during winter, the great height of the land surface of Spain results in extensive chilling of the air, which in turn leads to the development of a local zone of high pressure, especially over the interior. So for several months on end in winter a local anticyclone may cover the interior of Spain; and depressions from the Atlantic travelling eastwards towards the Mediterranean are diverted. They may pass northward, reaching the Mediterranean by the Bay of Biscay and Carcassonne gap in France; or southwards via the Straits of Gibraltar. At such times the greater part of the Iberian plateau becomes covered by a mass of cold, stagnant air, at a relatively high pressure. Mild, rainy winds are consequently excluded, or restricted in influence to the northern, western or southern coastlands.

The occurrence of the temporary zone of high pressure over Spain results in a reduction of winter rainfall, and an intensification of cold, since on the east and south of the peninsula winds tend to blow in a clockwise path round the centre of high pressure. This brings cold and often relatively dry air from central Europe into Spain. Another factor which also tends to reduce rainfall is the fact that even if a well-developed depression moves across the Iberian peninsula from the Atlantic, the south-easterly winds that normally blow in front of the advancing depression may originate over North Africa, and hence be warm and dry. In north-west Europe, the comparable south-easterly winds develop over sea areas, thus adding to the total rainfall of the depression. But in Spain, the south-east quadrant of a depression can often be unusually dry, sometimes in fact even scorching. The name *Leveche* is given to winds of this kind, and they occur at all seasons, but especially late winter.

On the other hand, the interior plateaux of Spain (which are mainly ringed by highlands covered in snow) can experience dry cold local winds of the 'mistral' type—i.e. clear, dry and bitterly cold currents of persistent and sometimes violent character produced by cold dense air sliding to a lower level. The Ebro valley is especially subject to cold winds of this sort.

In the summer season a high-pressure zone centred over or near the Azores extends north-westwards towards Europe, and often covers much of the Iberian peninsula. Over the greater part of Spain, winds tend to be from the north; and the dry nature of the air greatly limits the formation of cloud. In consequence, the sun can beat down uninterruptedly. Summer temperatures are hence remarkably high, especially in the centre and south of the peninsula. Almost everywhere Spain experiences at least one day each year when the thermometer reaches 100° F., and temperatures of 110–115° F. are known even at Bilbao and La Coruña. The Plain of Andalusia, the hottest part of Spain, normally experiences 115-120° each year, with extremes of over 120°.

The effect of almost unbroken high-pressure conditions in summer is to exclude most of the Atlantic depressions, and deflect them far to the north. Consequently, June, July and August are almost (but not entirely) rainless over most of Spain. In the extreme west and north, however, where

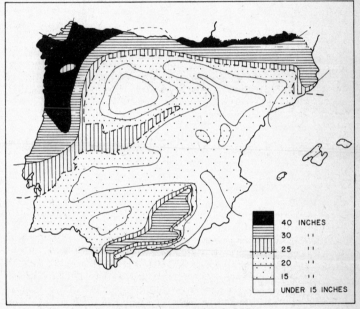

40 INCHES
30 ''
25 ''
20 ''
15 ''
UNDER 15 INCHES

4 Iberia, Annual Rainfall

winds can more frequently blow directly off the sea, there is a more regular rainfall—with as much as 5-10 ins. during the three summer months—in Galicia and the Basque coastlands.

A special feature of summer in much of central and southern Spain is a prevalent dust-haze—fine dust particles being lifted up by the heated air as it rises from the surface of the land. This phenomenon, common during July and August, is spoken of as 'la calina'; and there is a well-known phrase (*hay polvo*—it's dusty) used in talking of daily weather.

Rainfall. As regards rainfall in general, Spain can be divided into two sharply contrasting regions: the rainy north and west, and the remainder of the country, known as 'España Secana'. In the former zone, the limits of which will appear from Fig. 4, as much as 40–75 ins. of rain fall annually (Santiago, in the wettest part of Spain, has 70 ins., with the highest mountain crests still more). Elsewhere in Spain, however, aridity is increasingly the chief factor, with the minimum annual rainfall ($4\frac{1}{2}$ ins.) occurring on the south-east coast near Almeria. The 25-in. isohyet (600 mm.) can be taken as a convenient line of demarcation between rainy and dry Spain: and from the extent of the dry area one can appreciate why aridity and civil war are spoken of as the twin curses of the country.

Snow. Despite its southerly situation, and the surrounding warm seas, the Iberian peninsula is in winter remarkably cold for its latitude. Snow is thus an important feature in the north, and by no means uncommon in the centre and south. A summary division can again be made—this on a line roughly east–west through Madrid, from Lisbon to Tortosa. South of this line, snowfall is almost unknown on the coast, and light in the interior, except on the higher mountains—though snow showers may occur in Madrid itself as late as May, or even June. Hence (bearing in mind the great heat of summer in Madrid when it eventually does arrive), the local saying that the climate of the central Meseta is 'winter for nine months, and hell for three'.

North of the line, snow falls regularly in most winters, and the Meseta has 10–30 days of snow (cf. London 13, Manchester 14). On the higher ground snow may lie to a depth of several feet for many weeks, and permanent snowfields occur on the mountain slopes. The highest passes across the Pyrenees are usually only open for four months in each year; and on the plateau of Old Castile communications can be interrupted by snowfall for several weeks in severe years.

CLIMATIC REGIONS

Three major climatic regions may be distinguished within Spain: (1) the 'maritime' area of the north-west, (2) the interior or 'continental' zone, and (3) the 'Mediterranean' régime of the southern and eastern coastlands.

The Maritime Zone. This comprises the Pyrenees, Basque lands and Galicia. Main features are a relatively mild winter with generally abundant rainfall; a warm (but not by Spanish standards hot) summer, with rainfall well spread throughout the year.

Considerable local variation can, however, occur. The southern sides of the mountain ranges are in general warmer and drier than the northern aspects—this is especially true of the Pyrenees—and the total amount of rainfall tends to decline from west to east, the controlling factor obviously being distance from the Atlantic. Consequently, the Eastern Pyrenees are much drier than the western parts; and there is a marked contrast between the French slopes and the Spanish side—the latter being distinctly sunnier and drier.

On the coasts of the north and west, winter temperatures range between 45° and 50° F., but inland the influences of altitude and also continentality are soon felt, so that Oviedo, 20 miles from the sea, is about 5° F. colder than the coast. The January mean at Pamplona (40 miles inland) is 38°—lower than that of Seattle or Portland, Oregon.

The opposite occurs in summer. Coastal areas have a mean of 65–70° F., and inland, conditions are 5–10° warmer, with occasional daily maxima of 85–100° on a few days each year.

Rainfall is on the whole abundant, and well spread throughout the year, with autumn (October, November, December) the wettest season. Amounts vary from 30 to 40 ins. annually on the coastlands, to 80 ins. on the higher, north-facing mountain slopes. No month is without rain; July, usually the driest time in all parts, has a fall of at least 1 inch in most areas. An important feature is that even in the drier parts of this climatic zone, rainfall is markedly regular from year to year.

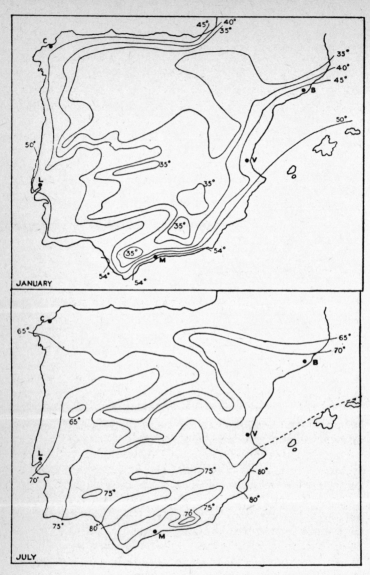

5 Temperature Conditions

There are very few of the drought years and seasonal fluctuations (as between one time of the year and the corresponding season of succeeding years) which are highly characteristic of the rest of Spain.

Also, owing to the definite, though moderate, summer rainfall, natural vegetation and cultivated crops are different from those in the rest of Spain—no other area has a reliably moist summer.

Because of the high humidity with prevalent off-shore winds, fog is common off the north-west coasts of Spain: the only part of the country of which this is true. La Coruña and Bilbao have fog on one day out of five or six: but a short distance inland where the mountain ridges tend to shut out moisture from the sea, the prevalence of fog and mist is much reduced.

The Continental Zone. This region, which can be taken as including the whole of the Meseta, the Ebro trough and adjoining mountain areas of the east and south, is characterised by remarkably wide variations of temperature. These occur firstly as between summer and winter (i.e. seasonally) and secondly, as between day and night (diurnal) at all seasons. Equally characteristic are the low and very irregular falls of rain, with high rates of evaporation. Except upon the upland ridges, annual falls are generally below 20 ins.

As we have already noted, winter in all areas, even the far south (New Castile and Badajoz), is a remarkably cold season, the unpleasant effects of which are at times enhanced by strong winds, and high humidities, all of which produce piercing, 'raw' conditions. The northern basin of the Meseta (Old Castile) has an average January temperature only one or two degrees above freezing point (this means frost on almost every night)—some 5–7° F. colder than conditions in Atlanta or Memphis. The district round Burgos is actually the coldest area (mountain slopes of course excepted), and here, 25–30° of frost can occur. Farther south, the January mean temperature is higher, ranging from 40 to 45° F.; but the uplands of the Central Sierras and eastern and southern barrier ranges are distinctly colder than this, as would be expected from the extra effect of greater altitude.

In summer, the lack of cloud allows uninterrupted heating by the sun on most days. Only about 15–20% of the sky is covered by cloud, and in many places over 150 cloudless days are recorded each year. Consequently, very high temperatures develop, with, as would be expected, the southern and eastern regions somewhat hotter than the rest. Even in the north of the Meseta, however, the July–August mean is 70° F., with day maxima normally touching 90–100°. In the centre and south, the average is 75–80° F., with day maxima 95–105°, and an occasional 110° F. After dark, though, the temperature may fall suddenly by as much as 30° F., bringing the night minimum to only 45–50°, which seems extremely chilly after the great mid-day heat. Hence the saying that the air of Madrid is so keen and subtle that though it will not blow out a candle, it will put out a man's life.

The Ebro trough by reason of lower altitude, which more than compensates for a northerly position, becomes extremely hot in summer—another, minor, factor being the almost completely encircling ring of mountains. Temperatures at Zaragoza can exceed 110° F., and close to the river itself high atmospheric humidity makes conditions even more oppressive. This however is a distinctly local effect, since in general humidity throughout the Ebro basin, as also on the Meseta, is low during the summer months.

The rainfall régime presents some anomalies and irregularities. In the northern basin of the Meseta, the Central Sierras and the Ebro basin, there are two separate rainy seasons: April to June, and October to November, separated by a relatively drier winter and an almost completely arid summer. Late spring is definitely the wettest part of the year, with the second (autumnal) peak of rainfall distinctly smaller in amount—a sharp contrast with the Maritime régime already described.

In the southern half of the Meseta (Badajoz, New Castile) the rainfall sequence is slightly different. There are still two separate seasons of heavier rains, spring and autumn, but the

spring rainfall maximum is earlier—March or April—and the
wettest season of all can often be autumn, not spring, as in the
north. An explanation of the double maximum rainfall general
throughout the Meseta may be sought in the changes of air-
mass which take place as the local high-pressure conditions
of winter break down and are ultimately replaced by the
spread of the Azores high-pressure system in summer. In the
intervening period before either of these systems becomes
fully developed (i.e. the seasons of late spring and autumn),
damper maritime air can penetrate from the surrounding seas
and reach the centre of the land-mass. The dry seasons in
central Spain correspond to periods of high pressure—being
consistent and well developed in summer, therefore with almost absolute aridity. In winter they are less continuous,
hence some, but not a large amount of, rainfall occurs.

Amounts of rain received over the Meseta vary according to
locality. Over the highest parts (i.e. the ridges of the Central
Sierras) total annual falls are of the order of 20–25 ins.; but
15–20 ins. is the average for most of the plateau-surface, with
as little as 11 ins. in some districts sheltered by mountain
ridges from maritime winds. Apart from a few local thunder-
storms produced by excessive heating, July and August are
almost totally dry.

A most important feature of rainfall in the Meseta region is
irregularity and unreliability. Heavy downpours may occur
over a small area, with neighbouring regions almost unaffected.
Then, too, annual totals fluctuate widely from year to year:
though the average taken over a period may amount to 15–20
ins., as little as 6 ins. has been known to fall in one particular
year. The entire period 1951–54 had almost no rain at all,
producing great economic distress.

Irregularity of rainfall is especially pronounced in the
southern half of the Meseta, particularly on the borders of
Andalusia. Periods of heavy torrential rains can alternate with
complete aridity—Granada has had 45 ins. of rain (250% of
its normal *annual* total) in one month. Such fluctuations of
flood and drought are a great handicap; and on the whole,
sudden flooding in a region normally arid, is apt to be more of

a disaster than drought, to which life in some respects has become 'conditioned'.

An explanation of the sporadic and irregular nature of rainfall is that it is normally produced from a 'Cold Front'. This is a condition arising when a wave of cold air penetrates into an extensive mass of generally warmer air. The clouds formed are very turbulent and of great vertical height, so that they can contain a considerable volume of water. But they are also of very restricted horizontal extent, so that the discharge of rain is concentrated over a small area. Moreover, this kind of cloud is greatly influenced by local topography, building up rapidly over highland, and soon breaking over plains or on the lee sides of hills. Cold fronts are known over Britain, where they usually produce squally, unsettled weather: but the greater part of British rainfall comes from an opposite situation—the Warm Front. Associated with the latter is the steady, moderate rainfall from layers of cloud that can cover hundreds or even thousands of square miles without much break. Warm fronts are not, however, very well developed in Spain—hence the general aridity of the interior, and the irregularity of such falls of rain as occur.

The 'Mediterranean' Zone. This can be considered as extending from the extreme south-west of Spain (the plain of Andalusia) along the southern and eastern coasts as far as the Pyrenees. The main features are a strongly developed rhythm of winter rainfall (with late autumn actually the wettest period); a lower general total of rainfall; generally higher temperatures both in summer and winter, and finally, a more limited diurnal variation, which in winter especially keeps the whole area distinctly warmer than in the interior.

Mean temperatures in January usually lie between 50° and 55° F., except in Catalonia, where owing to a more northerly position and the proximity of the snow-covered Pyrenees, temperatures are about 5° lower. Occasional hot spells can occur at this season—70° F. is recorded from time to time, usually when southerly winds from Africa develop. The coastal stretch immediately east of Gibraltar as far as Cabo de

Gata is the warmest region of Spain in winter, and here most January days experience a day maximum temperature of 65–68° F., with frost quite unknown. Farther to the north and east, frosts can occur: and occasional spells of cold (with temperatures near 32°) are an important handicap to the 'huerta' cultivation in the coastal strip between Cartagena and Valencia, where most of the crops are of the sub-tropical variety.

The inland situation of the plain of Andalusia is reflected in slightly lower winter temperatures (i.e. a greater degree of continentality). Frost is very rare—though not totally unknown —on the coast near Cádiz; but not uncommon at Seville and Córdoba. In these latter areas day temperatures can be as high or even higher than those near Gibraltar: 70° F. is recorded on one or two days of January in most years.

In summer, temperatures are of course high, although the sea acts as a slight mitigating influence. The hottest region of all is that farthest from the sea—i.e. between Seville and Córdoba, which is known locally as the 'African frying-pan'. Here the mean July–August temperatures are 85–88° F., and day maxima occasionally reach 112–115° F. Along the coasts of the Atlantic and Mediterranean, day maxima rarely exceed 100° F., and the mean drops to 72–80° F.

An important feature is the low atmospheric humidity of the summer months. This, also characteristic of southern France and Italy, is what one might normally expect, and it makes the great heat more bearable. But it should be noted that in many other parts of the Mediterranean—e.g. Malta, North Africa, the Levant coasts, and part of Asia Minor— atmospheric humidity can be very high during the summer months, making living conditions unduly oppressive. Spain is fortunately spared this condition, except very locally in the Ebro valley.

A further feature of Mediterranean Spain is the liability to hot easterly or south-easterly winds: the *Leveche*. These, originating over North Africa, are hot and extremely dry currents which sometimes contain fine dust. The same kind of wind is spoken of in Italy as the sirocco. Such winds are most marked in spring, when they may cause considerable damage to growing crops. Whole fields may be withered in a single day. Another easterly wind, strong and boisterous, but cooler and moist, is the *Levante*, which is due to a funnelling effect between the Betic mountains of Spain and the Atlas of North Africa. A current is drawn westwards from the western basin of the Mediterranean through the Straits of Gibraltar towards the Atlantic.

Rainfall is generally slight, often insufficient. Normally, amounts received range from 15 to 25 ins., with however very marked local variations controlled by aspect, topography and nearness to the sea. At Gibraltar, 35 ins. fall annually, but 200 miles away at Cabo de Gata the yearly total is only 9 ins. Variability from year to year is also an important characteristic. Annual incidence at Seville can vary from 6 to 34 ins., and 5 ins. have fallen in one day, and 15 ins. in one month. Thus, as farther inland on the Meseta, capriciousness in onset of rainfall, with considerable liability to local floods, is a prominent feature of Mediterranean Spain—even more so, in fact, than on the Meseta. Spring is the season of widest weather variation in temperature and rainfall. One day is wet and cold, the next perhaps really warm and fine, with unexpected alternations. The autumn, on the other hand, displays more regularity: e.g. though at Valencia August is normally the driest month of the year, September is equally regularly the wettest. It should also be stated that the summer is not completely arid. In parts of the north and east there is a slight, but significant, rainfall. Over the extreme south and east, however, summer falls are negligible—once again a reminder of the geographical affinities between Spain and North Africa.

Chapter 4

SOILS AND VEGETATION

SOILS

THE natural factors controlling the development of a particular kind of soil are (1) type of underlying, or parent rock, (2) climate, and (3) topography. It might at first be thought that rock type would alone influence the nature of the soil that occurs upon it; but this is far from true. In fact, the greatest influence is that of climate, and the same parent rock can give rise to quite different soils according to moisture and temperature conditions prevailing.

In a cool and humid climate, the soils are frequently 'leached'—i.e. the relatively large amounts of rainfall, unreduced to any marked degree by evaporation, percolate downwards through the soil, dissolving out soluble minerals and carrying away non-soluble elements, both of which tend to be removed from the layer near the surface. Under hot and arid conditions, the opposite effect occurs. Mineral salts are dissolved for a time by scanty, but locally heavy rainfall, and then a long period of heat and drought may draw the soil moisture back to the surface, where it is evaporated, leaving a concentration of minerals—especially salts of calcium—in the upper layers.

The distinction between leached or 'podsolised' [1] soils, and 'pedocals' (those that accumulate calcium compounds near the surface) is most marked in Spain. Throughout pluviose Spain, podsols are characteristic; whilst in the drier and warmer parts of the country, pedocals are the dominant soil type. This division, closely reflecting climatic conditions, is the fundamental one in classifying the soils of Spain. However,

[1] This word is Russian, as are many others in soil-science.

this simple distinction is not the whole story, since there are also several other kinds of soil, e.g. alluvium and mountain soils. Moreover, sub-types occur within the two broad groupings of podsol and pedocal.

The podsols found in Spain are of the kind known as 'Brown Earths'. These are dark brown in colour, often with a greyish tinge, slightly acid, and of an open, granular structure. It would seem that these brown earths developed originally under temperate deciduous forest-land; and such soils occur widely in north-west Europe. In Spain, the brown earths are naturally best developed in the west and north, extending as far south as Extramadura, and the lower slopes of the Sierra Guadarrama in the east. Though it would appear that like the other brown earths of Europe, they too once supported a forest cover, the present natural vegetation found upon them is *matorral*—a drought resistant scrub of bushes and thorn plants.

The pedocals are characterised by alkalinity, a closer (clayey) texture, and a general redness in colour—browny-red in the wetter parts, where they merge into brown earths, and brighter red where temperatures are higher and rainfall more sharply seasonal. To the bright red soils the name *Terra Rossa* is given. These latter soils are specially·characteristic of the Mediterranean lands, as they develop best under the climatic régime of hot dry summers and wet winters.

The true Terra Rossa areas of Spain extend from Murcia eastwards and southwards along the Mediterranean coast; whilst the duller red soils extend into Aragón, Catalonia and the south-eastern parts of the Meseta. Both types of soil are fertile if sufficiently watered. But unfortunately they are especially liable to erosion, and Spain has very greatly suffered in this way, more so than any west European country.

In a few places where rainfall is very scanty and temperatures high, the pedocals cease to have a red colour, and become grey or even white, owing to the very high concentration of soluble salts at the surface. These are saline soils, which are sterile, and useless for cultivation. Such soils are really characteristic of hot deserts; and their occurrence in Spain is restricted to a few localities only where the climate is unusually hot and arid (La·Mancha), and where the parent-rock is rich in soluble minerals—e.g. the gypsum beds of East Andalusia or the Ebro valley. Nevertheless, the presence within Spain of saline soils even on a very restricted scale, is once again a reminder of African affinities.

Three other types of soil may be briefly mentioned. In regions of high relief, or on steep slopes, soils are very thin, coarse in texture, and deficient both in soluble minerals and in humus. Such mountain soils are obviously unrewarding to the farmer, but owing to the topography of Spain, they are very widespread.

An opposite condition occurs in Valencia along the coast where short but very active rivers flowing through regions of widely varying rock-type have laid down small and local patches of exceedingly deep and rich alluvium. This is a heavy black soil, with much humus and a moderate, but not too high mineral content, evenly distributed throughout the layer. A rather similar, dark clayey soil also occurs on certain of the Guadalquivir river terraces in Andalusia. These are comparable in fertility with the famous black soils of Texas and the Indian Deccan: and the two black soils of the south and east to some extent explain the reputation of Andalusia and Valencia for agricultural richness.

NATURAL VEGETATION

It is somewhat surprising, in view of the relatively harsh climatic conditions of Spain, to note that the Iberian peninsula has a variety of flora wider than that in any other region of comparable size in Europe. This situation is due firstly to the different climatic effects prevailing. There is a range from almost Equatorial conditions in a few sheltered river-valleys in the south-east to, on the one hand, tundra conditions on the higher mountain slopes, and on the other, to the steppe or even salt-desert conditions in parts of the interior basins. Moreover, Spain's plant-life has been greatly enriched because of the country's geographical situation, as a bridgehead between

Africa and continental Europe, and as a pier stretching towards the New World. Spanish interest in the Americas has resulted in the introduction of several American and a few Asian plant species that have now become well acclimatised. At a broad approximation, some 25% of the natural vegetation of Spain can be said to be purely native to the peninsula, and a further 20% 'Mediterranean'—i.e. shared with neighbouring lands to the east and south. About 40% is central European or Alpine by origin, 8% African and 4% American and Asiatic.

The distribution of plants within Spain is strikingly controlled by climatic conditions. In the north and west there is a natural vegetation complex broadly similar to that of northern and western France, Ireland and Britain—on the drier parts a fairly thick forest cover of oak, chestnut, beech (now reduced in many places), passing into open grassland in the damper lowlands. On the higher plateau surfaces heathland, heather and peat-bog are common; whilst at higher levels still, larch and conifers appear, until, towards the mountain summits, the zone of true Alpine vegetation is reached. The Spanish Pyrenees, higher and distinctly drier than the highlands of Cantabria and Galicia, have a slightly different tree cover. The forest growth is less dense, and above 5000 ft. altitude pines and firs predominate.

Much of the interior of Spain has a special and distinctive type of vegetation, known as *matorral*. This is a complex of evergreen or thorn bushes and shrubs, sometimes low, sometimes as much as 10 or 15 ft. in height, occasionally interspersed with dwarf oaks or conifers. The *matorral* can take many forms, approximating in the wetter and colder parts to a real woodland, and in the drier zones to a thin thorn scrub. In certain parts, broom and gorse together with oaks and thorns can produce an especially dense form of *matorral*. This is much the same as the French *maquis*; and, like its counterpart, is (or has been) notorious in providing shelter for bandits or those 'agin the government'.

When less luxurious (i.e. consisting mainly of thyme, lavender, mastic and myrtle) the *matorral* can be compared to the *garrigue* of France. Soil character has some influence on growth, besides the dominating factor of climate. On siliceous (siallic) rocks, which tend to give acid conditions and therefore (with sufficient rainfall) a podsol, the thicker *maquis* tends to occur. Low scrub is more characteristic of the limestone (i.e. pedocals). Particular kinds of *matorral* have distinctive names: *tomillar* (thyme predominating), which is common over the southern basin of the Meseta, and *retamal* (broom), best developed on the Central Sierras around Madrid.

Steppe. Where annual rainfall totals less than 15–20 ins. the *matorral* gives way to steppe conditions. These are expanses of bare soil thinly covered by patches or tufts of coarse inedible grass, thorns or dwarf bushes. Here and there, edible grass flourishes for a few months annually (as in the steppes of Central and south-west Asia), and provides several weeks' grazing for farm stock. But in many parts aridity favours the growth of esparto, too stiff and dry for fodder, yet useful as a cash-crop for export, or locally in the making of sandals. Esparto grass steppe covers many square miles in the east and south of Spain.

Where there is indeterminate or inland drainage, or where saline soils occur a distinct complex of salt-tolerant scrub is found: tamarisk and saltwort, once again reminiscent of North Africa or south-west Asia.

Mediterranean Flora. Towards the east and south coast, from the southern fringes of the eastern Pyrenees as far as the Andalusian lowlands, vegetation types are distinctively 'Mediterranean'. Even as far west as Portugal, the local 'Atlantic' flora shows a slight intermixture of Mediterranean forms; and these latter gradually become dominant towards the east. The main elements of Mediterranean vegetation are evergreens (laurel, cork oak), various dwarf pines, together with low-growing shrubs, bulbs and thorns. Towards the extreme south, dwarf palm trees become fairly numerous. Where rainfall is relatively abundant, as on the southern flanks of the Pyrenees, a true forest-growth occurs (cork oak, eucalyptus and pines); but in the drier parts (as in Murcia and Valencia) the natural vegetation is little more than scrub.

Forests. Both natural physical evidence (soil type and geomorphology) and literary and archaeological impressions point to the probability that at one time Spain was fairly thickly forested. Most highlands were in all likelihood covered by deciduous forest (in the north and west) or by evergreens. But uncontrolled cutting (for which the coldness of winter is one explanation), over-grazing by sheep and goats (which destroys new growth), and less likely, a change of climate within historic time[1]—have greatly reduced the woodland cover. This now extends over less than 10% of the area of Spain, as compared with 25% of Portugal.

CULTIVATED VEGETATION

The same pattern (with a major distinction between pluviose and dry Spain, resulting in a broad diagonal zonation from north-east to south-west) is apparent in the distribution of cultivated crops. The 20-inch isohyet and the north-western limit of olive growing almost coincide; and in Spain the northern limit of the olive is also almost exactly the southern limit of the birch tree—an indication of the sharp transition from cool maritime (Atlantic) to Mediterranean conditions.

Once again, the north and west stand apart as a separate region. Meadowland, sweet chestnuts and maize are the principal cultivated vegetation types. The reasons for the dominance of maize as a cereal are the generally high summer temperatures, together with abundant moisture throughout the growing season, continued, as heavy showers, through high summer.

On the Meseta, and over most of south and east Spain, wheat is the principal crop. The main area of wheat growing is in the north-west basin of the Meseta, round Valladolid, where the dry (but not too dry) and relatively cool summer,

[1] It would in the writers' view be erroneous to ascribe much importance to this last element.

together with open terrain and a good soil, are especially favourable factors. Other areas where large amounts of wheat are produced are the Madrid–Toledo region, Zaragoza province, La Mancha, and the southern slopes of the Betic Cordillera round Málaga. In this latter district specially early varieties are grown, with harvesting well before the maximum heat of summer. Wheat is produced in all provinces of Spain, with

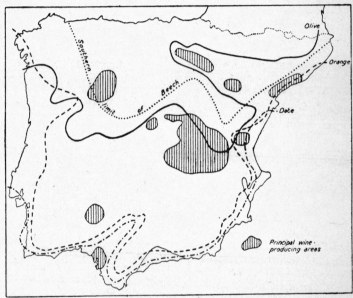

6 Limits of Plant Distribution in Iberia

however only insignificant quantities in the north-west provinces previously discussed.

Barley is much more tolerant of heat and aridity: its cultivation therefore tends to be more concentrated towards the south and east. In one province, Murcia, it outranks wheat as the most important cereal crop. Elsewhere it is definitely subsidiary to wheat; and in the north-west, its importance is very slight. Most barley is used as animal feeding-stuff, either dry, or as green fodder.

Another fodder crop is oats, which in Spain are grown either on marginal land—too cold, too dry, or with a poor soil, or else as a subordinate crop in the poorest part of a cereal rotation involving also wheat and barley. Hence the distribution of oat growing is irregular—generally small quantities in the north-west, south and east, and most in the central lands of the Meseta. The chief oat-growing province is in fact Extramadura.

Rye is similarly a subordinate rotation crop (to wheat and

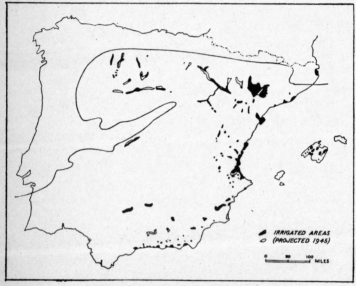

IRRIGATED AREAS
(PROJECTED 1945)

0   50   100   MILES

7 Irrigated Areas and Projected Schemes

maize) in regions of marked cold and damp. Thus its distribution is fairly sharply restricted to rainy Spain—chiefly Galicia and along the northern frontiers with Portugal. Salamanca is the main rye area: and besides its use as a cattle food (and sometimes as an adulterant or substitute for wheat flour) the straw is used for thatching and for making twine.

Rice-growing is restricted to parts of the warm eastern zones where abundant irrigation water is available. A mean temperature of at least 61° F. during the entire growing season is essential, and so frost in late spring is particularly dangerous. Valencia and the Ebro delta round Tarragona are the main rice-producing areas, and Spain is one of the few European countries to be self-sufficient in this cereal. Yields per acre are far higher than for any other cereal—2 tons being normally obtained as compared with $\frac{1}{4}$ or $\frac{1}{3}$ of a ton per acre for other cereals.

An important sector of Spanish agriculture is that concerned with leguminous crops—chick-peas, alfalfa, clover, vetch, lupins, lentils, beans and peas. These are grown as regenerative crops in rotation with cereals. Owing to the aridity of soil in many areas, leaving land fallow after reaping an 'exhausting' cereal crop does not improve soil quality as quickly as is the case in cooler and more humid lands. If the land is simply allowed to 'rest' without any crop it may lose what little moisture it has—a vegetation cover retains moisture. Also, because of their nitrogen-fixing properties, the growing of legumes is well suited to Spanish conditions. Some of these plants are used as cattle fodder, others for human food. The chick-pea is a staple diet in much of Andalusia and Castile, the former area being the chief producer in Spain. Beans are common all over the country, but most extensively produced in the south (Andalusia, Granada, Extramadura) whilst peas are also widely distributed—predominating in the Meseta and eastern coastlands.

Tree and Bush Crops. The olive and vine are by far the most important crops of this category, but other fruit—apple, chestnut, orange, etc.—are also significant. A common feature, found in many Mediterranean lands, is the interplanting of lines of fruit-trees with cereals and other crops.

In terms of area planted and yield, the olive ranks as the most important fruit grown in Spain. Its distribution is, however, sharply restricted to the centre, south and east: rainy Spain is not suited to olive growing. The tree thrives best on thin rocky soils, with only a minimum of water. Heavy watering produces a fine tree, but no oil. The olive can stand some, but not too much frost (hence its extension into the Meseta), and a long hot summer is essential. Andalusia and the lower Ebro basin are the main olive areas of Spain, with Jaén as the principal 'olive town'. The tree grows wild in the Meseta and south to heights of 5000 ft. Both Andalusia and the lower Ebro have been renowned since Roman times as exporters of oil; but most olive oil is, however, retained for home use. Because of the lack of animal oil, the olive provides the chief source of fat in human food. Consumption is about 35–40 lb. per head of population annually—about ⅔ of a pint per person per week.

The vine needs a dry, well-drained soil, and is tolerant of cold winters. Limiting factors are a low summer temperature and heavy autumnal rains. Consequently the vine is grown to some extent in almost every province of Spain, but the main areas are along the east coast: Catalonia, Valencia and Almeria especially, with another important region in La Mancha.

In most areas, grapes are grown for wine and its by-products, and only 5–10% is used as dessert fruit. Spain ranks as the third wine-producing country of Europe (after France and Italy); and whilst most Spanish wine is of indifferent quality and used locally as an everyday beverage (like French *vin ordinaire*), certain districts have a high reputation for wine making.

The 'Huerta'. No statement on crop-growing in Spain would be complete without some reference to the 'huerta' system of exploitation. Originally developed by the Moslems,[1] the 'huertas' are small, highly cultivated plots which depend on irrigation water brought by an intricate system of channels, aqueducts and lifts from rivers or springs. The 'huertas' were placed so as to take advantage of topography and the special fertility of certain soil types; and skilled treatment over many centuries maintains crop yields at a level far higher than that elsewhere in Spain. The most densely populated agricultural zones are those of the 'huertas'. Crops grown range from vegetables

[1] The Arab name for this kind of land utilisation is a *vega*: the Latin origin of the Spanish term (*horta*) will be apparent. *Vega* is still used in Andalusia and parts of Valencia.

(onions, asparagus, capsicums, carrots, spinach and artichokes), to fruits of many kinds (strawberries, melons, pomegranates, figs, oranges and vines), and cereals (chiefly but not exclusively rice), together with sugar (cane and beet), tobacco, and even groundnuts and bananas.

Frequently, there is a local tribunal, a Water Court, to adjudicate on usage and allocation of the irrigation water, consisting usually of local farmers, sometimes also a priest or government official, or a land-owner. Such practices are frequent in regions where water supply is scanty, and once more recalls a parallel with Arab lands of Asia.

Part II

THE HUMAN BACKGROUND

Chapter 5

HISTORICAL GEOGRAPHY

THE first evidences of human settlement in Spain go back to the earlier phases of the Ice Age. During periods of milder climate (the 'interglacials') the lower river valleys were occupied by scattered groups of primitive (Lower Palaeolithic) man, who lived by hunting, fishing and the collection of edible fruit, berries and insects. At times of colder, moister climate, open areas were abandoned in favour of caves.

The Neolithic (New Stone Age) involving agriculture and hence a more settled, easy existence, was of great importance in Spain. Associated with it are two remarkable sorts of monument: the world-famous cave paintings at Altamira and elsewhere, and the construction of great Megalithic monuments, partly for burial of the dead, and partly for ceremonial purposes. Later still came the use of metals. Copper, and afterwards bronze, reached Spain about 2000–1500 B.C., with iron-working about 800 B.C. The mining and refining of metals was greatly stimulated by the activities of Phoenician traders and colonists, who after the 13th century B.C. came to exert an extremely pervasive, if not predominant, influence upon eastern and southern Spain.

The Phoenicians, and their descendants, the Carthaginians, were a people of Semitic racial type originally from the eastern shores of the Mediterranean, in what is now the Lebanon. They also had important colonies in present-day Tunisia and Algeria, and under their impulse trading posts and later colonies were established in Spain. Mining of copper, silver, lead and salt were developed, with some stock rearing in the plateau areas.

Somewhat later in time (*c.* 8th–7th centuries B.C.) Greek colonies also came into existence along the Mediterranean coasts of Spain. Usually at bitter enmity with the Phoenicians and Carthaginians, the Greeks in particular fostered the cul-

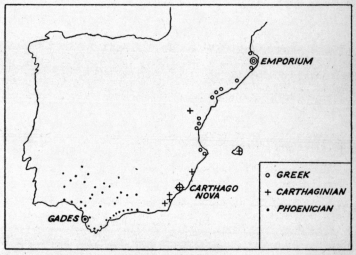

8 Early Settlement

tivation of the vine and olive: but their influence, though by no means unimportant, was less pronounced than that of the Phoenicians or Carthaginians (Fig. 8).

Parallel with the Semitic and Greek occupation of southern and eastern Spain was the entry of quite dissimilar racial groups into the north. The arrival of the Basques (see Ch. VIII) is a mystery; but there is evidence that at least as early as the 8th century B.C. a long-headed (dolichocephalic) and slightly-built race, known as the Iberians, were in possession of much of the centre and north of Spain. Their spread was checked by the arrival from Central Europe of the Celts, who reached

Spain during the 5th–4th centuries B.C. Like their counterparts in north-west Europe, the Celts seem to have been of distinctly varied racial character, many markedly tall and fair, but some darker, and shorter in height. The way of life of these people seems to have been broadly similar to that of the Celts of France and Britain—tribal, pastoral and patriarchal, with an impulsiveness of character and fondness for warfare.

Hence over the period 700–200 B.C. Spain could be regarded as having a rough zonation of peoples and stages of development. In the southern and eastern coastal margins a high standard prevailed with much international contact, and substantial Semitic and Greek racial elements. Elsewhere, towards the north and west, living conditions became gradually more primitive, the lowest levels occurring in the Cantabrian and Galician hills. Here a poor subsistence economy prevailed, with frequent inter-tribal warfare.

THE ROMAN PERIOD

Carthaginian domination of the south and east of Spain was ended by the Punic Wars, which resulted in the final defeat in Spain of the Carthaginian leader Hannibal in 206 B.C. For another 300 years the north and west sporadically resisted Roman arms, but after A.D. 133 revolts entirely ceased, and Spain remained content as a Roman province. During four succeeding centuries Iberia experienced less war or political disturbance than any other area of the Empire—an indication of its geographical isolation from the main currents of activity, and also of the thoroughness of Romanisation.

Roman Culture in Spain. This flourished most in the south and east, and again the north and west remained, as in Phoenician days, at a markedly lower level of development. One major change due to Roman influence was the incentive to urbanisation. Old defensive hill sites and fortified highland towns declined, as newer trading and administrative centres grew up on the plains near river crossings and port sites. At first Gades (Cádiz) was the leading town of Roman Spain but, later, lost pre-eminence to Tarraco (Tarragona), and then Malaca (Málaga) and Barcino (Barcelona).

Other leading towns were Hispalis (Seville) and Corduba (Córdoba). The fact that all but one of these towns were ports reflects the importance of overseas commerce in Roman Spain, particularly that with Italy. As early as the reign of Augustus (co-eval with Jesus Christ) the inhabitants of some fifty Spanish towns had full or partial rights as Roman citizens—a privilege not lightly given at that epoch.

Economic. Spain is spoken of by Roman writers as a land of considerable and diverse riches. Agricultural produce, animal products, minerals and manufactures are the items most mentioned, with approximately 30% of the total area given over to cereal growing, and a further 5% to the production of fruit and olives. Spain was for long the principal source of olive oil within the Roman Empire.

Forest may have covered as much as 40% of the total area: certainly timber was a principal item of trade, and the mines of the period made use of the large quantities of wood, both as pitprops and as fuel for refining the ores. This may account for some of the deforestation, soil erosion, and degeneration to scrub now characteristic of present-day Spain.

The extent and scale of Roman mining in Spain is astounding. Besides extending previously existing mining sites, new ores were developed, and some ancient waste-heaps still provide raw material for modern extraction plants. Greatest interest centred on the Sierra Morena (where Roman galleries 4 miles long are known), but other mining districts were the lower Ebro, central Andalusia, Cantabria and Galicia. Copper, lead, gold, silver, tin, iron, antimony, manganese and mercury were exploited, and the richness of Spanish ores is also indicated by the long history of working—the Rio Tinto and Almadén areas being conspicuous but by no means isolated examples of exploitation extending over centuries and even millennia.

Effects of Roman Occupation. Despite some regional differences in the degree to which Roman ways were adopted, the Roman occupation brought about certain lasting effects upon the human geography of Spain. For the first time, the whole peninsula came under a unified rule, with one predominant language, a simple system of law and government, one single fiscal and customs system (a feature not common in Roman administration) and a level degree of economic activity that reduced the traditional disparity between the 'advanced' Mediterranean lands and the primitive centre and north. The Latin form of speech became the basis of a later national language—only in the Basque country did native speech remain unaltered. Though the influence of a 'dead heart' within the Meseta continued, this was distinctly reduced by the road systems crossing the centre, and by the coastal trading which brought the north and west into closer direct contact with the rest of Spain. The advances of the Roman period provided a guide and example to later rulers, who laboured to re-create the single unit of Roman times: and the geographical similarities between parts of Spain and metropolitan Italy fostered the growth of a tradition almost identical with that of Rome itself.

VISIGOTHIC SPAIN (5TH–8TH CENTURIES A.D.)

The end of Roman influence in Spain came almost exactly at the same time as the withdrawal of Rome from Britain. In A.D. 409 an invasion of Vandals, Alans and Suevi from central and northern Europe led to the occupation of Galicia, Andalusia (the name comes from the Vandals) and the Mediterranean coastal zones. Five years later a group of Visigoths (also from northern Europe) conquered Catalonia; and over the next sixty years established predominance throughout Spain, crushing the Suevi and Alani, and expelling the Vandals.

The Visigoths were relatively few in number, and disposed to leave existing Roman ways of life and government largely unaltered. They were not unacquainted with Roman culture, and had acquired a form of Christianity known as Arianism.

This belief was fiercely denounced as heresy by the native populations of Spain, who followed a Western Catholic orthodoxy under the leadership of the Pope. Although some Visigoths were converted to Catholicism, religious fanaticism was a feature, with severe persecution of one sect by another—Arians, Catholics and Jews (who were at that time numerous). The weakness of later Visigothic kings led to a rise in the effective power of the clergy, with ecclesiastical leaders (especially Catholic) playing a decisive part in political and everyday affairs—a feature that has persisted in Spain down to the present day. Gradually, however, the strength and vigour of the Visigothic ruling class declined: and the effect was to reduce the country to a confused pattern of petty warring states—a Spanish Dark Ages.

THE ARAB PERIOD

In the year 710 came the first Moslem invasion from North Africa, led by one Tariq.[1] Little serious opposition was encountered, since dynastic quarrels between Visigothic princes, an oppressive social system involving serfdom and slavery, and severe religious persecution prevented effective union in the face of Moslem invasion. Many of the common people of Spain were ready to acquiesce in a change of masters.

Within two years the central Meseta, Ebro valley, and parts of León and southern Galicia were occupied, and in 720 an Arab army poured into France, reaching its farthest point, the banks of the Loire, in 732. Here, at Tours, a battle was fought against a Frankish army under Charles Martel, resulting in a defeat of the Arabs, and a retreat southwards. By 760, Islamic occupation of western Europe had recoiled to the Pyrenees.

It is important to note that during this attempted conquest of France, parts of north-west Spain remained quite unsubdued. The highlands of Galicia and the Asturias, difficult of access, unattractive in climate to the Moslems, and unrewarding economically, were ignored and by-passed in the rush towards

[1] The landing took place at Gibraltar = Jebel Tariq (Tariq's Hill).

the Pyrenees and France. Among the Asturian uplands Christian resistance continued, based on a kingdom with a capital near Oviedo, and from this district in the Asturian mountains began the long process of Christian re-conquest.

Elsewhere, however, Arab rule flourished, despite some faction and disturbance, and the gradual loss of certain northern provinces. For the centre and south of the peninsula the 10th century A.D. came to be a golden period of Moslem rule, during which Islamic culture reached a level markedly above any elsewhere in Europe. This pre-eminence lasted for nearly two centuries, during which the Spanish Arabs made important material, and outstanding intellectual contributions to European civilisation.

Causes of Moslem Superiority. The Arab territories of the 9th and 10th centuries A.D. had a relatively numerous and wealthy population, in sharp contrast to conditions both in northern Spain and the rest of Europe. This was due partly to a highly advanced system of agriculture, and a productive, broadly based craft industry. Agricultural methods first developed by the Arabs in south-west Asia were introduced into Spain, where a similarity in geographical environment particularly favoured the transition. The basis of the system was an intelligent pattern of small-scale irrigation channels taking advantage of the variations in slope and aspect of the eastern and southern uplands of Spain, where melting snows and springs occur in close proximity to small but fertile low-lying areas.

The garden-like character of cultivation in the south-east has remained to this day: Arab influence still colours agricultural practice in this part of Spain, with the names 'huerta' and 'vega' markedly prominent.

Cereals (chiefly wheat and barley) were the principal crops, with vines, olives and oil-seed grains; but in addition the Arabs produced an extensive range of fruits, and also mulberry trees (upon which silk worms fed), cotton, madder and saffron—the last two being used as dyestuffs. Besides the indigenous Mediterranean fruits, Arab farmers are credited with introducing into Spain the Asiatic plants rice, cotton, sugar, apricots, peaches, pomegranates (i.e. Granada apples), and the Seville orange. An enlightened system of share-cropping, with the produce equitably divided between owners and peasants, encouraged initiative more effectively than did the feudal system of Christian Europe.

Mineral resources—gold, silver, iron, lead, tin, copper and mercury—were also exploited, as the basis of an important manufacturing industry. Toledo became a leading European centre of fine steel-making for arms and armour (by hand, of course, and in small quantities) and was especially noted for its damascene work (i.e. inlay of gold and silver on other metal, originally developed in Damascus). Paper making was introduced from south-west Asia, for the first time in Europe, and proved a most important factor in the intellectual predominance of Moslem Spain (see below). Textiles (in cotton, merino wool, silk and mohair), glassware and pottery were also important products of Moorish Spain. Most of all, however, the leather industry of Córdoba had a continent-wide reputation.

With this basis, a flourishing export trade was carried on from Seville, Cádiz, Málaga and Jaén. Spanish products were greatly prized not only in Europe, and the Moslem world of Asia, but also beyond—in India, China and Russia. As further indication of the commercial importance of Arab Spain, it may be significant to note that for nearly 400 years, Christian Spain had no currency of its own, but relied mainly on Moslem coins. The extent of Arab connection with seaborne trade at the period is shown by the following words, originally Arabic, which have passed into general use: arsenal, admiral, average, cable, tariff, paper.

Moreover, Moorish Spain was at this time the intellectual centre of Europe. Philosophy, poetry, music, architecture and history were greatly cultivated, and Moslem models influenced Thomas Aquinas and Dante, besides probably contributing to the development of the epic poem and lyric in northern Europe.

The Arabs were also ahead of Christian Europe in various scientific studies: astronomy, mathematics, botany, medicine and alchemy—the forerunner of chemistry. In addition, the works of Spanish Arab geographers are still read today, both for their treatment and matter: Islamic geographers developed the 'regional' as distinct from the 'systematic' approach to the subject. Among the principal writers were: Ibn Khaldun, a Court Official at Granada, who wrote on history, geography, social organisation and the relationship of geography and history; al-Bakhri, a native of Córdoba, who drew up regional statements in the form of inventories: Ibn Jubayr, who described in detail the geography of a pilgrimage from Granada to Mecca; and al-Idrisi, whose critical appraisal of facts, insistence on the sphericity of the earth, and high level of cartography rank him as the greatest geographer of the Middle Ages.

Most probably the greatest contribution of Arab Spain to European culture was in the preservation and transmission of ancient Classical works, chiefly Greek. The works of many Classical writers would have been lost but for Arab interest during the early Middle Ages—for some centuries Euclid could be read by Europeans only in Arabic—and the general European Renaissance would hardly have developed had there not existed Arabic editions of Classical texts in literature and science. Greek, Latin, Persian and Hindu authors, with Arab and Jewish-Arab commentaries, survived until early modern times, and served as standard text-books in most European universities until the 16th century. It was from studying Arabic translations of Eratosthenes and Ptolemy, together with later Arab geography, that Christopher Columbus reached the conclusion that the earth was round, and hence that Asia could be reached by sailing westwards from Europe. It would also appear that from Moslem Spain came certain of the ideas, and many of the teachers, that contributed to the founding of universities in Europe. Teaching institutions broadly of university character existed in Córdoba, Seville, Málaga and Granada, and attracted scholars from all over Europe, among them Roger Bacon, Michael Scott, and Adelard of Bath. From Spain, the idea of a university spread into southern Italy, where Moslem models were explicitly acknowledged.

We may in conclusion attempt to assess the importance and significance of the Moslem occupation upon Spanish culture and national development. Opinions on these points differ. At first, about a century ago, there was a tendency to ascribe much in modern Spain to Arab influence; then, after 1898, a reaction set in, with a minimising or even denial of the importance of 'the Moors in Spain'. Now, as the reader of the immediately preceding paragraphs will gather, there is once more a heightened appreciation and emphasis of the legacy due to Islam.

Another divergence of opinion occurs over the actual effects of the Moslem conquest. Some Spanish historians see in the occupation a wholly regrettable event, for three reasons. In the first place, Christian Spain, which might otherwise have evolved in the way later taken by France, England and Italy, become involved in a disastrous sequence of war and internal unrest. Before the Moslem conquest, Spain was at least as advanced as France, and far ahead of Britain, Italy and Germany; and, if left undisturbed, the whole Iberian peninsula could have developed into a rich and powerful unified state. But Spain's destiny to carry the brunt of the Moslem attacks on Europe deflected the national energies at a supremely critical time; and Spanish nationality was thus the principal casualty. Spain, so to speak, defended Europe at the cost of her own advancement, and the 'Moorish interlude' was a major calamity, in that it canalised all human activity within Spain towards militarism and a sterile unproductive obsession with warfare.

A second line of thought suggests that the long period of warfare bred in both combatant groups an exacerbation of religious feeling. From singlemindedness, Spanish religion passed into intolerance and fanaticism. The Christian clergy were thus able to gain a position of strength and influence far beyond that achieved in any other European country; and the real interests of Spain then suffered from the excess of ecclesiasticism which resulted. In the words of a modern Spanish historian (E. S. Alburnoz), 'Spain sacrificed to Catholicism both liberty of spirit, and greatness as a nation.'

Finally, some other Spanish writers argue that the circumstances of the Moslem invasion and Christian Reconquest fostered regional particularism to excess. Just as the sporadic risings of subject Christian populations in the Balkans against the Moslem overlords produced only a heterogeneous mosaic of small states that are renowned for disunity, so the Reconquest of Spain 'balkanised' the Iberian peninsula, with disastrous consequences that still persist—isolation, differing local traditions and recurrent civil wars. Others, however, see in this regionalism carried to excess the influence of geography pure and simple, together with the habit of mind of the Spanish people.

Chapter 6

MEDIAEVAL AND MODERN SPAIN
A.D. 700–1920

THE history of Spain can be divided into five main episodes. The first is concerned with the rise of the Northern
Kingdoms, with Spanish expansion from mountain fastnesses
into the foothills overlooking the interior plains. The second
episode is that of the 'Reconquista', the freeing of Iberia from
the Moors. This episode, the longest in Spanish history,
has left its mark on the whole landscape of Spain even to
the present time.

From A.D. 1250 to the end of the 15th century the story is
of the development of the Spanish State, of settlement and
consolidation. Before the State had matured the fourth episode
—that of the Empire—had opened. From 1492 to about 1920
we see the Spanish people involved in geopolitical developments for which politically, socially and economically they
were not prepared.

The last period, that of modern Spain, has not yet ended—
it is a period of recovery from imperial decline, of empirical
struggling towards national unity and stability.

Throughout these episodes, there is to be observed an amaz-
ing continuity of geographical influences. Indeed in Spain
more than in any other part of Europe does a geographical
approach to history become rewarding.

The Rise of the North. The mountains of rainy Iberia were
inhabited by a number of people who, out of the welter of the
Dark Ages and the Moorish conquests, were to form the Spanish
national state.

These tribes, each with its own nuclear mountain region,
lived in remote and difficult environments and maintained a

rather savage independence. In the extreme west lived the Galician groups around their tribal centres of the bland western foothills. Their eastern neighbours inhabited the more rugged mountain lands of the Asturias. The small coastal plains and inland depressions of Cangas de Onís and Oviedo served as the rallying points for all the cordilleran peoples between Galicia and Navarre. From them and from Galicia came the first southward surge. In the Central Pyrenees lived the mountain pastoralists of the Four Valleys around the Val d'Aragón and of Sobrarbe, in some of the wildest and most desolate mountain country in Europe.

These hill peoples of Galicia, Asturias and the high Pyrenees were the makers of Spain. At times overshadowed by the power and wealth of their richer neighbours of Navarre and the Catalan coast, their creations of Castile and Aragón finally dominated and absorbed the other groups.

Navarre, lying across the western spurs of the Pyrenees, was the land of the Basques, who inhabited the fertile lowlands around Bayonne in the north and Pamplona to the south, the hill country behind Guernica. They controlled the Pyrenean passes of Roncesvalles and Ispeguey, also the coastal routeway. Early asserting their independence, the Navarrese from the middle of the 11th century onward became too closely associated with France, too involved in European political entanglements, too content with their pleasant homelands to become a dynamic part of the Reconquista.

Catalonia was very much a Frankish outpost, the heart of the Spanish mark maintained by the Merovingians and Carolingians. The Counts of Barcelona owed allegiance to the French Crown, and their interest lay in Roussillon and the Rhônelands rather than in Iberia. From Ribagorza to Barcelona natural orientation was northwards across the Pyrenees, and eastwards oversea.

By A.D. 750 Moorish domination of Galicia and the plains of Léon had collapsed. Asturian raids down to the gates of León devastated the cultivated areas and by 'rescuing' large numbers of the Christian population produced an almost empty 'cordon sanitaire' around the north-western mountain heartlands. Behind this screen was re-formed a kingdom of Galicia.

As Moorish control of this least Mediterranean part of Spain crumbled away, the mountain pastoralists moved into the plains of León and beyond. By A.D. 790 the tribal capital had been moved from Oviedo to León itself. A faintly surviving Visigothic tradition helped to hold together the associated kingdoms of Galicia, Asturias and the new León in spite of successional and personal problems. The believed discovery at Compostela of the bones of St James, long the patron saint of the littoral people, brought added unity and strength. To the new shrine of Santiago came pilgrims and ecclesiastics from many parts of Europe, bringing culture and learning to rude and remote people. Above all they had a common environmental heritage, of a maritime hill climate, of forests and streams, of pastoralism.

In the misty hills and valleys a rude plenty of crops and livestock supported a vigorous population able and ready to move as independent frontiersmen into the interior. By the end of the 8th century they were poised along the south-facing foothills from the Douro mouth past the upper Esla to the Ebro headwaters.

While in the north-west the stage was being set for the first surge of reconquest, little was happening along the line of the Pyrenees.

In the east the Counts of Barcelona held precarious sway of the coastal plains and hills. The natural poverty of this region was sufficiently noteworthy to give to its first ruler Wilfred the title of 'Comes Vellosus'—the hairy count—because his land was covered by poor scrub forest. In the Central Pyrenees of wild and difficult mountains a no-man's-land existed, where poor villages were able to support no more than a meagre existence, disturbed occasionally by armed forays from both north and south.

Only in the richer lands of Navarre was there established a vigorous political unit. Even here independence was periodically imperilled by the Navarrese tendency to use control of the western passes of the Pyrenees as a bargaining weapon. By

A.D. 750 Navarre was still confined to the old lands of Basque speech.

The Reconquista. The difference between the vigour of the kingdoms of the Cantabrians and the weakness of the Pyrenean states became especially marked during the first two centuries of the reconquest.

From León and the Cantabrian Cordillera by A.D. 950 armed ranchers had spread into Vardulia, the upper basin of the Douro, and their fortified farms and peel towers (by courtesy called castles) gave the region its new name of Castile. Burgos, a pre-Roman route-centre settlement, became the heart of the new frontier province.

Old Castile is environmentally transitional between arid and pluviose Spain and the new settlers had to modify rather than revolutionise their modes of life. Water-supply was more restricted than in the homelands, but on soils less leached than those of the forested hills cultivation gave good results except in times of extreme drought. Summer pasture was poorer than in the mountains and cattle gave way to sheep, but transhumance already practised in the north was extended to overcome this difficulty. The trees and crops were still mainly those of Atlantic Spain—the beech, chestnut and apple rather than the orange, olive and vine; rye and wheat rather than barley. On the other hand away from the riverine areas 'extensive' land use predominated, and nucleated settlement developed in response both to environment and insecurity. In Old Castile the influence of the Meseta began to play its later more dominant rôle.

Farther to the east Spanish expansion was still slow. The 9th century disintegration of the Carolingian Western Kingdom emphasised the natural weakness of the peoples of the Spanish Mark. Moreover, the Moorish Kingdoms of Zaragoza and Lérida based on the richest lands of the Ebro basin put up stiffer resistance than did the poorer disaffected Berbers of Castile and the west. The Aragonese peoples by 950 had established outposts no farther than mountain towns such as Jaca. Huesca still lay beyond their grasp, and the scorched

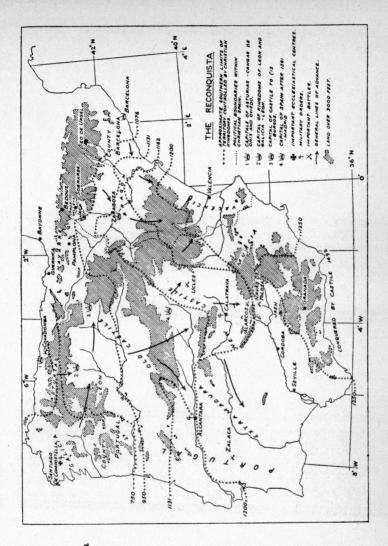

9 The
Reconquista

flats of the Ebro tablelands over which they looked were less inviting than were the plains of the Douro.

Between A.D. 950 and 1140 this contrast between west and east reached its climax. The general limits of Moorish occupation had been pushed back approximately to the line of the olive—farther in the Atlantic lands—by 1131. The Counts of Castile had assumed a crown and the leadership, and Burgos and Valladolid became acknowledged centres. Along the Atlantic littoral a practically autonomous County of Portugal extended south to the Tagus. The Central Sierras were crossed and conquered, Toledo becoming the frontier post of a New Castile that included most of the plains of the upper Tagus.

The Ebro basin remained longer in Moorish hands. Isolated from Castile by the difficult Iberian mountains, Zaragoza remained inviolate from the West, and a re-formed Aragón, based on a nucleus in the Pyrenees, was as ready to attack Christian Navarre and Castile as the Moors of the lower Ebro.

The detailed historical reasons for lack of unity between the Christian kingdoms do not concern us here, but the facts and their consequences are of importance. The lack of Spanish coherence was only surpassed by the social and political disunity of Moslem Spain. Factional alliances of Christian and Moor were common. The Cid himself, posthumously regarded as a crusading paladin, actually spent more of his life in adventuring in support of Moslem princes than in advancing the cause of Christendom.

We must therefore conceive of a great zone of frontier Spain developing in the insecurity not of frontal warfare but of anarchy. In these stormy circumstances of political and military inconstancy local interests grew more strongly than the power of any central authority. The military nobility and the crusading orders of Santiago, Alcántara and Calatrava struggled for their own power. New and old townships wrested from frequently weak kings the 'fueros', their rights to local municipal law. They also allied themselves in the 'hermandades' (brotherhoods) against predatory nobles.

This mediaeval anarchy was by no means peculiar to Spain

but the tragedy lies in the fact that it has never wholly been suppressed down to the present day.

Regional distinctions had firm roots in environmental differences. Every successive advance southward merely increased the heterogeneity of each kingdom. Between Castile and Aragón and Castile and Portugal appeared the contrasting outlooks of the Meseta and the sea lands, one centripetal, the others centrifugal. The old nuclei remained the conservative custodians of tradition, the new settled lands developed the ferment of novelty.

Equally important was the exaltation of the restricted interests of each estate above the general interest of society as a whole. From this strong insistence on sectional representation born out of political instability can be derived the element of egalitarian syndicalism which even now plays such a large part in Spanish life.

This evaluation of the parts as being larger than the whole survived for two main reasons. First, before unity could be achieved, Spain was plunged into adventures in Europe, North Africa and the Americas. Secondly and more fundamental is the non-appearance of any strong nuclear interest. The regional contentiousness so clearly present in this early period was never overcome by the discovery of a new centralising attraction. With only mild exaggeration can it be said that with the move into New Castile, very nearly the poorest and most sterile of the major regions becomes the heart of Spain. With so weak a nucleus sectional as well as regional feelings could remain strong.

After recovery from the shock of a temporary Arab resurgence, the Spanish kingdoms once more marched forward. Moorish victories at Zalaca and Uclés served more to encourage unity among the Spaniards and to strengthen the crusading element in the Reconquista than to delay the southward surge.

In 1164 Aragón and Barcelona were united, with fateful consequences for both. Aragón became involved in Catalan interests in the Mediterranean and more infected with Frankish feudalism. The Catalan spirit of independence in turn was strengthened by the accretion to the coastal strip of the Ebro hinterland. Without this union Barcelona might have become a peripheral but still closely associated region of Castilian Spain. With the union there appears the Catalonia of recent history, a large nation within a state, not only suspicious and resentful of Meseta control but also powerful enough to assert its individuality.

By this time Aragón with Castilian help had conquered Lérida and Zaragoza, and annexed part of a declining Navarre. The first treaties for the delimitation of Castilian and Aragonese zones of conquest had been made, reserving to Aragón the Mediterranean littoral and its immediate hinterland south to Valencia. By 1245 Aragón had expanded almost to its fullest extent.

During the same period Castile was confronted with a severer struggle. At three keypoints Castilians and Moors maintained outposts. In the west at Alcántara the Cistercian Military Order of that name strove as fiercely for entry into Extramadura and the lower Tagus lands as did Wellington for nearby Badajoz seven centuries later. This key region from Zalaca onward had a longer and bloodier history than most. In the east Cuenca overlooked the route down the river Júcar from the Meseta to Murcia. Here too from Uclés onward a threshold region is marked by battlefields.

In the south, between the Guadiana and the Sierra Morena, lay the third and most debated zone. At Calatrava first the Knights Templar and then the Cistercian Military Order provided the firm base for Castile. Jaén and Córdoba were the Moorish bases. Between and around these points clashed armies for several centuries until at Alarcos in 1195 Castile suffered such a crushing defeat that, urged on by the Pope, all the Christian kingdoms of Iberia formed a Crusading alliance. They poured over the pass of Despeñaperros and in 1212 finally crushed the military strength of a temporarily unified Caliphate at Las Navas de Tolosa.

To this day, the naturally poorest regions of Spain, Extramadura and La Mancha bear witness to the severity of the struggle that raged in these frontier regions. Least attractive

to Moors and Spaniards alike they had been the least developed. Almost completely depopulated, they were but slowly
resettled.

By 1250 the Reconquista was practically over. A weak
Moorish Kingdom of Granada still sheltered in the mountains
of African Spain but this, like the individual Moslems of the
conquered territories (the 'mudéjares'), existed on sufferance.

The cost of the reconquest was enormous. For half a millennium the wealth, labour and attention of the Kingdoms of the
North had been directed towards war. The population density
of Spain remained the lowest of any European country until
the 16th century, the economy the most 'extensive'. The only
obvious fruits of the fight were the vast outpourings of his-
tories, lyrical and epic poetry, legal and scientific treatises
during the 12th, 13th and 14th centuries.

THE SPANISH STATE

From the middle of the 13th century onward Spain had
no longer anything to fear from Islam. The conquest of
Granada, the absorption of a vast number of non-Christians
and the long struggles against the corsair kingdoms were by
no means easy but proved slight compared with new problems
of consolidation and expansion.

In Castile consolidation was the keynote. Slowly the lands
devastated by war and disorganised by conquest were brought
under control. The population was small and ill-equipped for
the task of exploiting new resources; the inhabitants of Castile
probably numbered no more than some three millions at the
close of the 15th century. Their conquests had been mainly of
the poor Meseta; and in Andalusia which was of greater
natural wealth the first consequence of the Reconquista was a
decline in the high level of productivity attained by the Moors.

The economic, political and social organisation of Castile
had evolved under relatively chaotic conditions, and reorgani-
sation was by no means completed in the little time available.
Sectional interests remained powerful, and Castile was made

up of a series of small autocracies and miniature republics over which the sovereign held troubled sway. Land was held in a variety of customary and legal ways in which feudal order was little observed. The Kings land ('Realengo') and the 'Salariego' (land of the nobles) waxed and waned relatively with the King's strength. 'Abadengo', the estates of the Church, grew more or less constantly in time. In status below these groups lay the lands of the towns, and of the peasants. The chartered towns by main force held their 'Comarcas' on which they depended for supplies. Those peasants unable to attain the wealth-status even of the lowest Caballero formed associations under elected nobles to whom they had to commend themselves, and on their 'Behetria' lands had surprising freedom. Real serfdom and slavery were very rare.

This relatively egalitarian society lies at the roots of the pride of every Castilian. Until population increased and economic pressures replaced military need, it worked well enough in maintaining local self-sufficiency. Castile remained an area of surplus and relative freedom until the colonies and European adventures imposed a drain on her resources which resulted in general impoverishment.

Political problems were considerable. Internally the Reconquista altered the centre of gravity within the state. Until 1087 the North remained supreme around the capital of Burgos. Between that date and the conquest of Granada Toledo was the court centre, a vital outpost and the richest and best developed Meseta town to be recovered from Islam. The nobility of Old Castile and the North resented the swing into leadership of the Tagus lands, and this in itself caused much unrest. After the final expulsion of Moorish power the greater wealth and importance of Old Castile reasserted itself as the southern Meseta was slowly occupied. The Court moved back to Valladolid and between that city and Burgos developed a bitter rivalry.

Externally, relations with Portugal and Aragón were by no means settled. In the main these conflicts were a natural result of the leading part played by Castile in the Reconquista, and of a reluctance to accept the existence of other Iberian powers.

The final frontiers seem now more geographically logical than they did to mediaeval sovereigns.

The Mesta. One of the most significant developments of this period is the rise of the Mesta. Early in the 12th century the name appears as a description of local meetings of shepherds, arranged in order to exchange strays from the flocks that had slowly spread across the sparsely populated arid central plains. A century later the Mestas were dealing with pasture rights of sedentary and migrant flocks and in 1273 Alfonso X called together a national association of herders. To this national Mesta were given certain responsibilities and privileges. The main migration routes from the winter pastures of New and Old Castile to the summer grass of the Cantabrian hills were defined, and three royal 'Cañadas' (or broad tracks), demarcated the Leonesa, Segoviana and de la Mancha. Officials of the Mesta dealt thenceforward on a national scale with all the problems attending the growth of a migrant pastoralism simultaneous with the spread of sedentary agriculture. The need for such an organisation and its evolution is a measure of the previous emptiness of much of the Meseta, and its accelerating occupation.

During the 13th century the summer export of wool through Cantabrian ports to Flanders and England grew to considerable proportions. In the 14th century royal recognition of the importance of the trade and encouragement of fine wool production further helped a pastoralism already adventitiously aided by plagues which reduced the cultivators' demand for land. The Mesta was heaped with privileges, and wool marketing strictly supervised, all in the royal interest. Wool meant bullion; and as in Tudor England the fleece was indeed golden.[1]

One fateful consequence was the establishment of a precedent for centralised control of trade, leading to the creation of staple towns with monopolistic powers. When the New World was discovered what more natural than the channelling of

[1] Cf. the institution of the Order of the Golden Fleece as the highest honour in the Spanish Court.

trade through similar controls? Thus, the Consulado of Burgos that finally handled most wool shipments became the model for the Casa de Contratacion at Seville that monopolised shipments to the Americas.

Without being too determinist, one might say that the harsh environment of the Meseta, that transformed the farmers of the Asturias into sheep-herders dependent on long-range transhumance, also left an indelible stamp on most Spanish economic activities at home and abroad.

In Aragón, conditions were very different. Smaller than the kingdom of Castile her population was probably greater. Around Zaragoza and Lérida and along the littoral south of Barcelona, a large settled population of many faiths and nationalities already occupied the intensively worked most fertile land. Here there was no problem of resettlement, but rather of absorption. Stemming both from the low status accorded to these conquered groups, and from Frankish influence, a true feudal organisation developed, lacking only an undisputed head. Almost as in France the practice held 'Nul Terre Sans Seigneur'. The nobility held land and vassals by right of military service. The church, also exempt from taxation, enjoyed considerable power. More important than in Castile were the strictly grouped mercantile, professional and artisan classes, together of considerable power in Catalonia. The peasants were generally in a state of serfdom, and increasingly bound to the land, while the Mozárabes (Christianised Moors), Mudéjares and Jews were usually either slaves or royal serfs.

Each of these classes predominated in one or other of the regions of the Kingdom, and were at conflict with the Crown and each other. The nobility of old Aragón and newly conquered Valencia represented the conservatism of the interior. Their alliance against the Crown, the Union of Nobles, sought to restrict royal power and also intrigued against mercantile Catalonia. The merchants of Barcelona in turn struggled for freedom from noble and royal interference, having little in common with the non-coastal areas. The peasants themselves, particularly of the 'huerta' zones, rose several times in open revolt against the 'Malos Usos'—the evil customs or harsh feudal dues.

These internal dissensions were aggravated by royal adventures in external affairs; and the weakness of the crown was increased by the conflict of reactions to oversea policy. From 1167 to 1258 the Kings of Aragón were involved in wars and disputes over territories in Provence—notably Montpellier. The Balearic islands became the attraction in the 1230's. The growing struggle between the littoral and the interior was typified by royal embarrassment in 1260 at a Castilian request for help in suppressing a revolt by Andalusian Moors. The nobles of old Aragón supported intervention, but the Catalans feared that such action might prejudice their good trading relations with the King of Tunis. Thenceforward Iberia mattered less in royal policy than did the Mediterranean.

The Empire of Aragón at its maximum extent rivalled that of Venice. Sicily was taken in 1282, Sardinia in 1324 and a Tunisian protectorate established in 1280. From 1327 onward Aragón was almost perpetually at war with Pisa and Genoa, her trade rivals in the Western Mediterranean.

Barcelona benefited from this imperialism, but the remainder of Aragón was bled white in the maintenance of armies and fleets. Even the Crown was weakened, in that the landed interests attacked every act of royal initiative and the Union of Nobles continually raised the banner of revolt. Moreover the very burgess interests that were being advanced clung tenaciously to their customary rights. In 1415 Ferdinand I when purchasing court supplies in Barcelona was forced to pay to the town taxes from which local nobility and clergy were exempt.

In spite of this relative chaos, progress was made. By the end of the 13th century one of the best courier services in Europe was operating, and by the close of the 15th century industries and communications were rapidly being developed and urban prosperity at least was considerable.

By 1479 and the accession of the joint sovereigns of Castile and Aragón, Isabella and Ferdinand, the states of Spain had only begun to establish themselves. But within twenty years Spain had to deal with an empire larger than Europe and the changes in world economy that followed the discovery of the New World and reduced Aragón to dependence on Castile.

THE SPANISH EMPIRE

Between 1479 and 1920, during the last episodic period in our survey, Spain both attained her apparent climacteric and sank to the nadir of her fortunes. This rise and decline, unparalleled in their magnitude, have been examined at length by many authorities, and all that can here be done is to indicate some of the factors involved.

During the whole of this period, Spain itself remained a poor and thinly peopled land. Population figures are significant:

1400 (estimate)	less than 6,000,000	
1600 (estimate)	8,000,000	
1700 (estimate)	9,000,000.	Cf. France 18,000,000
1857 (census)	15,500,000	
1897 (census)	18,000,000	
1930	23,500,000	
1960	30,000,000.	Cf. France 46,000,000

At the height of Spanish power towards the end of the 16th century, by far the largest proportion of the total population of under eight millions was engaged in agriculture. Unfortunately for Spain the strict control of agrarian life imposed by Ferdinand and Isabella was used for the sole benefit of sheep farming. Murcian and Andalusian high-farming inherited from the Moors was discouraged by taxation; town lands (both common and cultivated) lost ground to pasture for migrant flocks; and, most serious, considerable deforestation took place. The desolation of Castile by forest clearing was followed by erosion and land abandonment even in the 16th century. Not until the 18th century efforts of Charles III, one of the most enlightened autocrats of that European era, was agriculture regarded as anything more than a hindrance to the wool-exports which brought in return the bullion which alone could support the imperial organisation. Only in the Levante did farming production not diminish seriously, and there—except for wine and silk—the dense 'huerta' populations left little surplus over consumption.

Urban and industrial growth, with two exceptions, was slow. In 1561 Madrid, then a rural centre for New Castile with a population of some 25,000, became the capital of Spain. Within a century its inhabitants had increased to 400,000, but its poverty of function was illustrated by an equally rapid decline to 150,00 by 1700. Unlike Barcelona, Madrid had practically no economic function other than that of a market town for a poor province and was purely an administrative seat of the Crown and court. The second exceptional growth was that of Seville, and that also was a result of violent centralising tendencies. All American and colonial trade was routed through this port and controlled by its Casa de Contratación. Population rose to over 200,000, supported by trade and processing industries. Again unlike Barcelona, Seville had its wealth thrust upon it and decline rapidly followed competition by Cádiz and, even more serious, by English and Dutch industrialists and merchants. For the rest, little was added to the Moorish inheritance—Cordovan leather, Toledan linen and steel. Even these activities diminished rather than increased in importance, and the towns themselves declined.

The internal weakness of Spain resulted in the main from three factors. First, Spain is fundamentally poorly endowed with resources. Mineral wealth was, and is, small, and contributed little even to the royal treasury. The pluviose north then as now was characterised by local subsistence farming, while the Meseta offered only slow and small returns to dry-farming cultivation. The southern lands were rich only as the result of skilled and intensive Oriental-type irrigation and horticulture. The wave of religious intolerance, that started in the expulsion of the Jews from Andalusia in 1483 and finally affected all persons of Moorish descent and culture was a national disaster. These peoples constituted a majority of the skilled

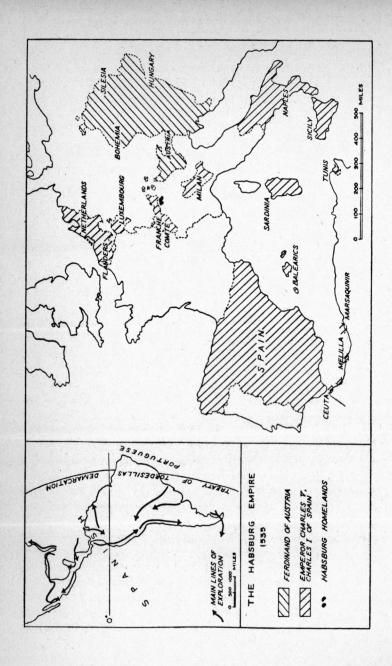

THE HABSBURG EMPIRE
1555

FERDINAND OF AUSTRIA

EMPEROR CHARLES V,
CHARLES I OF SPAIN

HABSBURG HOMELANDS

MAIN LINES OF EXPLORATION

0   500   1000   MILES

TREATY OF TORDESILLAS

LINE OF PORTUGUESE DEMARCATION

SPAIN

SILESIA
HUNGARY
BOHEMIA
AUSTRIA
NAPLES
SICILY
MILAN
TUNIS
NETHERLANDS
LUXEMBOURG
SARDINIA
FLANDERS
FRANCHE COMTÉ
BALEARICS
MARSAQUIVIR
MELILLA
CEUTA
SPAIN
MILES
0   100   200   300   400   500

'huerta' farmers and urban artisans outside Catalonia, and the loss of their experience considerably decreased the effectiveness of resource use.

Secondly, primitive regionalism and syndicalism had not been outgrown before the need for unity became greatest. The wars of Philip II were supported almost entirely by poor Castile, and by American treasure. Aragón held by her federal rights and contributed little, Catalonia opposed all ventures. The Cortes, the nobles, and municipalities even during the height of absolutism continued the old internecine struggle of individualism, and a Crown involved in foreign ventures could not dominate. The contrast with Tudor England is striking.

Thirdly, the rise of the Spanish Empire in Europe and in the Americas was in itself a cause of stagnation and decay. Through the Aragonese succession Spain became a European power. Ferdinand's grandson, King Charles I (better known as the Holy Roman Emperor Charles V) ruled over Spain, the Habsburg empire in continental Europe, and the Aragonese Mediterranean lands. The 'miraculous' year of 1492 saw the conquest of Granada, and the discovery of the New World by Columbus while attempting to discover a western route to the Indies. The Treaty of Tordesillas, set forth in a Papal Bull of 1494, claimed for Spain all territories 100 leagues westward of the Azores.

In 1535 the dominions of the Habsburg brothers, Charles V and Ferdinand of Austria, formed the largest empire that the world had seen (see Fig. 10). The tragedy of Spain lay in the fact this empire impoverished rather than enriched the motherland. From the time of the accession of Charles V to the death of Philip II in 1598 Spain was engaged in almost continuous European wars. The pride of Charles led him to attempt the overthrow of France, and to further conquests in Italy. The absolutism and religious fervour of Philip who could say 'I would rather reign in a desert than over a country peopled with heretics' led to the revolt in the Low Countries, embroilment in the French religious struggles, and war with England. The strain was too great. The colonies demanded foodstuffs

10 The Expansion of Spain in the 16th Century

and manufactures that Spain was unable to supply except at a cost of rising home prices and oppressive taxation. Between 1568 and 1570 Granada was desolated by revolts and in 1591 Aragón rose against Castile. The bullion which reached Spain from the New World—shipments of silver averaged over 300 tons per annum—was drained away even more quickly. In the virtual absence of any other than Catalan mercantile experience, foreign financiers, industrialists and merchants proved indispensable. By 1650 Genoese, German, English and Dutch entrepreneurs not only controlled most of Spain's external trade, but also about 80% even of internal trade and industry. In order to support Imperial armies, colonial expansion and even domestic consumption, the credit of the Crown and the colonies themselves were mortgaged to the great banking houses. The Fuggers of Augsburg had a monopoly of the export of wool, timber and iron. Venezuela was for a short time sold to Hamburg bankers.

Thus even at its political apogee Spain was already displaying real weakness. The reigns of the last three Habsburg monarchs was a period of further unrest and decay. Literature and science achieved their golden age under courtly patronage, but all else declined, and from 1665 to 1713 Spain was only saved from dismemberment by English and Dutch intervention against French ambition. Militant regionalism reared its head even at the beginning of the Bourbon period; and Aragón, Catalonia and Valencia had to be reconquered by Castile. By 1787 Madrid and Barcelona were the only towns with populations of over 100,000. Probably over one-quarter of the land lay fallow, with another half under forest and scrub. Mediterranean 'huertas' were still notable for their wine, fruit and oil, and Barcelona experienced an industrial and commercial revival in the 18th century. The rest of Spain dissolved into isolated and primitively self-sufficient regions.

During the Napoleonic régime and its 19th-century aftermath the same internal themes may be observed. During French occupation Spanish regionalism and sectionalism found their justification in that the nation deprived of central leadership fell back on local organisations. Town and country organised 'juntas' which demonstrated gloriously how strong local feeling could be. Their ineffectiveness in combination forecast troubles to come.

The National Cortes convened in the patriot stronghold of Cádiz in 1810 was the first of the quasi-liberal bodies that appeared.[1] Local revolts were regional rather than true liberal uprisings, and the final revolution of 1820 (which significantly centred on Cádiz) was quashed with French aid. Cádiz, which had triumphed over her rival Seville mainly because of her superior position for navigation, had become, as Barcelona earlier had been, a mercantile and middle-class centre. Like Barcelona it could not hope for success against the poor conservative interior.

The American colonies were in no better case. The crude mercantilism that proved so destructive within Spain encouraged unintelligent exploitation abroad. Too much emphasis was placed on the getting of negotiable treasure, too much on control of trade. Up to 1748 only two fleet convoys were annually allowed to sail between Spain and the Americas. The Spanish monopoly of colonial trade exercised by Seville and Cádiz was paralleled by the restriction of trade to three American Atlantic ports, Havana, Vera Cruz and Porto Bello.

What else could be expected? An Imperial Government that could destroy rather than utilise the enterprise of Antwerp, and an inexperienced Castile that could not control its periphery, were hardly likely to show great political or economic foresight. The colonial Empire, for which a penurious Spain emerging from the Reconquista was not ready, started crumbling into revolt in the 1740's. By 1826 the mainland American colonies were independent and by 1899 the last vestiges of the Spanish empire outside Africa had disappeared.

From 1833 to 1920 the political history of Spain ran in the old vein. The general acquiescence shown by the politically and economically immature rural population was continually disturbed by sectional and regional unrest. Conservative

[1] It may be recalled that the actual word 'liberal' is Spanish.

upland Navarre and Aragón, and the individualist Basques and Catalans formed a heterogeneous group hostile to the Central Government and passing under the name of 'Carlists'—supporters of Don Carlos, a proponent of absolute monarchy and a dominant Church. The result was anarchy. Republicanism, federalism and military dictatorships under the crown followed one another, the only constant being regional and class refusal to allow anyone to govern.

Much, however, was changing. The population almost doubled in size during the 19th century. The greatest rates of increase were in Madrid, the Vascongadas and Catalonia; the lowest in the rural centre. Improvements in the use of agricultural resources were slow for obvious reasons. The 'Secano' land, fit only for dry-farming, was not capable of great improvement. Technical advances allowed a diminishing length of bare fallow, but on the 'latifundia' shortage of capital and knowledge, and the natural lack of enterprise shown by the landless labourers robbed large-scale organisation of its theoretical advantages. In the old 'huerta' regions yields were already high, and the extension of irrigation required regional co-operation and national capital that were not available. Even so, farming production was increasing by over 2% per annum —a higher rate than that of population growth.

The greatest progress was being made in manufacturing and extractive industries. The iron ores of Vizcaya, the lead and the copper and iron pyrites of the Sierra Morena, the mercury of Almadén, known for centuries, became of great value only when the industries of Europe developed their great appetite for raw materials. From 1870 onwards these minerals and the coal of Oviedo replaced the traditional exports of wines, fruits and vegetables. In the Asturias and in Vascongadas they also formed the basis of a new industrial and urban life, still peripheral but no longer conservative.

In Catalonia, mainly after 1887, developed a true industrial revolution. The Barcelona Exhibition of 1888 was the first occasion of generation of electricity, and by 1920 the province of Barcelona was using half the national power production. Following the mid-century break-down of central authority, this old industrial and mercantile region re-emerged from relative stagnation. Textile manufactures, processing of agricultural goods and port industries, all using the new source of power, made rapid headway and in 1924 Barcelona took the population lead from Madrid.

These last developments bring the history of Spain up to the modern period and explain why 1920 is the date chosen to close an episode. From 1920 onwards a new and important estate showed its strength. The peripheral regions of Asturias, Vascongadas, Catalonia and Valencia became even more distinct as urban development and the growth of an industrial proletariat proceeded. The individualism of Catalonia becomes not only something cultural, something mercantile but also radical and impatient. Madrid itself becomes unrepresentative of the Meseta.

During the 500 years before the discovery of the New World the pattern of the historical geography of Spain during the succeeding near-half millennium had already appeared: central poverty and peripheral relative wealth; mountain pastoralism and the Mesta; the swing between the Atlantic and the Mediterranean; even involvement in external struggles.

The inability of the Meseta to become a true nucleus became more and more important. Unlike Paris and Berlin, Madrid had to attempt to rule without being really able to tie to her the other national regions—centralism without real centralisation.

Chapter 7

ECONOMIC GEOGRAPHY OF MODERN SPAIN

B ETWEEN 1920 and the present day much has developed
in modern Spain. From 1936 to 1939 the country was rent
by Civil War and her recovery was distorted by the impact of
World War II, but in spite of these difficulties much has been
achieved.

Covering an area of 196,000 square miles—more than twice
as large as Oregon or Wyoming—Spain with 30 million inhabitants has a low density of population compared with the
rest of Europe—one-quarter that of the U.K., one-third of the
Italian density, lower even than that of Yugoslavia.

A population density map of Spain (see Fig. 11), although
much is concealed in provincial averages, is extremely reveal-
ing. In arid Spain lack of water for reasons of climate, soil, or
topography makes anything but very sparse and nucleated
rural settlement impossible. Only in a very few areas has
mineral wealth proved sufficiently attractive to encourage
town growth. On the other hand, where water is available then
population density rises to oriental levels and concentration,
limited only by competition for land. In Catalonia alone has
a combination of rural wealth and trade caused any real urban
growth.

In pluviose Spain rural settlement is limited only by winter
harshness operating through altitude and aspect. Neither in
volume nor in value of production do the lowlands approach
the Levante in fruitfulness, but carrying capacity is still extremely high. Where, as in Vascongadas, mineral wealth and
manufacture coincide with beneficent conditions of climate

and terrain, then population densities are high and settlements of varied function appear.

The general pattern of distribution is essentially one of concentration in the peripheral coastal regions, but it must be emphasised that even this belt is discontinuous. The contrast between the densely populated seacoast and the sparsely peopled interior is particularly marked in southern Spain. Along the line of the Sierra Morena and the south-eastern bevelled edge of the Meseta and the Iberian mountains close settlement suddenly gives way to emptiness. The irrigated lands of the lower Guadiana, the mining areas of Rio Tinto and Henares, and the metropolitan district of Madrid, these alone form populous zones in the southern Meseta. Madrid, with a population of 2,450,000 has in some ways contributed to the prevailing sparseness by drawing to itself migrants not only from the poor countryside but also from old towns such as Toledo.

Although rural depopulation has proceeded unchecked for over three hundred years leaving some areas (as around Salamanca) virtually uninhabited, the northern Meseta has a population density only 20% smaller than that of New Castile. As noted in Chapter X the environmental transition between the Biscayan coast and the interior is comparatively gentle, and no sudden change in regional densities is noticeable. More important is the contrast between the dispersed settlement of the Atlantic regions and the nucleated centres of Old Castile.

In the north-east are some of the greatest extremes of population density and some of the greatest detailed variations. On the saline unirrigated lands of the Ebro is to be found almost complete desolation. The 'huertas' of Zaragoza and Lérida, on the other hand, carry population densities of over 200 per square mile. In Catalonia industry and trade, as in the Basque lands, have added a large urban population to rural settlement already dense in the lowlands. The Pyrenees, lightly settled in the foothills, are almost empty above the 5000-ft. contour.

1. Mountain regions
    1. Asturias—Pastoralism, rye, cider
    2. Pyrenees—Pastoralism, wheat
    3. Central Sierras—Summer sheep pasture, oats
    4. Iberian Mountains—Summer sheep pasture, oats
    5. Montes de Toledo—Barley, oats

2. Pluviose Northern Spain
    6. Pontevedra—Maize, dairy cattle, vines, pigs, potatoes, horses
    7. North Galicia and Asturias—Potatoes, dairy cattle, rye, apples, horses
    8. Vascongadas—Mixed farming

3. Western Spain
    9. West León and Salamanca—Rye, potatoes, carobs, cattle, sheep, wheat, asses
    10. Extramadura—Sheep, oats, pigs, goats, mules, olives
    11. Huelva—Fighting bulls, fruit, wheat, sheep

4. Central Spain
    12. Old Castile—Wheat and sheep
    13. New Castile—Wheat, sheep, barley, mules
    14. La Mancha—Wheat, vines, barley, goats, mules

5. Eastern Spain
    15. Ebro Basin—Wheat, sheep, vines
    16. La Rioja—Vines and mixed farming
    17. Zaragoza—Fruit and vegetables—Irrigation
    18. Lérida—Olives, sugar beet, vegetables—Irrigation
    19. Gerona—Cattle, wheat, horses
    20. Catalonia—Vines, nuts, vegetables

6. Mediterranean Spain
    21. Castellón—Carobs, oranges, wheat, barley

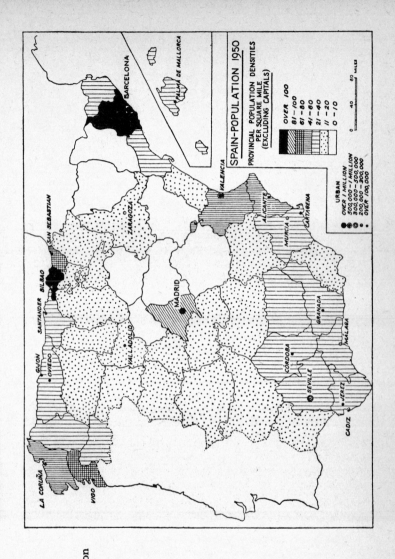

11
Population
Densities

SPAIN-POPULATION 1950

PROVINCIAL POPULATION DENSITIES
PER SQUARE MILE
(EXCLUDING CAPITALS)

OVER 100
81 – 100
61 – 80
41 – 60
21 – 40
11 – 20
0 – 10

URBAN
OVER 1 MILLION
500,000 – 1 MILLION
300,000 – 500,000
200,000 – 300,000
OVER 100,000

0   40   80   MILES

22. Valencia and North Alicante—Oranges, rice, potatoes, vegetables—Irrigation
23. South Alicante and Murcia—Barley, lemons, vines, dates, potatoes, sugar cane, esparto grass

7. Andalusia

24. Almeria—Barley, wheat, mules, goats. Grapes in littoral
25. Málaga and Cádiz—Wheat, barley, legumes, olives, mules, sherry, goats
26. Southern Seville and Córdoba—Olives, pomegranates, pigs, barley, wheat, mules, goats
27. Seville—Olives, wheat, fruit, cotton

8. The Balearics—Fruit: citrus and figs, almonds, wheat, barley, olives

AGRICULTURE

A population map of Spain as described above is in the main also a map of the carrying capacity of agricultural resources. These resources are by no means great, and their utilisation only appears inefficient when unfairly compared with other better favoured lands. The cultivated area, in Madariaga's words, 'duly corrected to take account of the excessive discretion which taxpayers are apt to evince in matters of land statistics', is probably about 45% of the total.[1] A similar area is covered with 'pastos y montes'—grassland and forest, of which the former largely consists of mountain pasture only seasonally usable, together with dry lowland herbage. The latter is for the most part scrub and coppice. Orchards and vineyards cover 17% of the cultivated area, a proportion in the 1960's only exceeded in Europe by Greece; and bare fallow another 20%.

These figures are illustrative not so much of extensive (or inefficient) land use, but of difficult utilisation. The high per-

---

[1] Salvador de Madariaga, *Spain: A Modern History* (New York: Praeger, 1958), p. 104.

centage of unproductive fallow land is a natural consequence both of aridity and of the length of fallow periods, which are very difficult to reduce. The extent of arboriculture is also ecologically understandable. These tree-crops (with the exception of the apple, citrus fruits and dates) have two especial virtues. The first, ecological, is that in common with the carob they are suitable for planting on broken terrain and are efficient extractors of groundwater. Their second virtue is economic: yields of sown crops are effectively lowered by the need for recurrent fallowing, but the tree crops mostly produce annually with only seasonal interruption. For these reasons they are found wherever they can survive local conditions. Because of the self-sufficient character of much Spanish farming, a self-sufficiency which arboriculture has strengthened, the limits of these tree-crops are only now beginning to retreat to areas of optimum conditions.

The sown crops show a similar regional distribution. Maize in humid and warm Pontevedra, rye of the higher granite soils of the north-west and potatoes of Galicia and the relatively humid Catalan hills, all reflect special environmental conditions. Wheat, the basic food-crop, is grown everywhere: this in itself is sufficient to explain why yields are low—in Portugal alone in Europe are they lower, and why they have not risen for sixty years. The normal 20th-century tendency has been towards tariff protected over-production, but since 1939 the struggle has been to reattain national self-sufficiency shattered by Civil War devastation. Success has now more or less been achieved. The regions of greatest importance for wheat and in which wheat is the dominant crop—not always the same thing —are the Castiles. In Old Castile the common bread wheats form the staple crop from Burgos to Zamora, in New Castile the durums almost monopolise land unusable for vines by reason of exposure to winter winds. Barley, the chief fodder crop, stands up better than wheat to aridity and has a shorter growing season. It therefore is a crop of the south, particularly of Murcia. The staple nature of these grains, their suitability for dry-farming and the coincidence of their rapid cycle of growth with the best seasonal climate—that of spring—explains their importance. They are only dominant when environment is too harsh for other crops.

Apart from the legumes, different varieties of which are grown everywhere, other crops are only important where thermal conditions are good and irrigation water available, viz. on the southern and eastern 'huertas'. Valencia produces almost 50% of the national onion crop, Tarragona one-quarter of the rice. Sugar beet is generally associated with the 'huertas' of Zaragoza and Lérida; sugar cane, now only of minor importance, with Málaga. Cotton cultivation is of greatest extent on the old marshlands of the lower Guadalquivir around Seville.

Livestock farming has still not recovered from the difficulties of the decade 1936–46, and, in that the larger stock are general-purpose animals and the smaller a natural part of every peasant's economy, statistics are not very meaningful. Cattle, particularly milch cows, are only of great regional importance in humid Atlantic Spain, where they form part of true mixed farming. Pigs and goats are everywhere found where woodlands and scrub give poor natural pasture, but in Galicia stall-fed lean swine are carefully raised, whilst in Andalusia the milking goat is equally cared for. Sheep are mainly associated with the 'secano' wheat lands and the mountains.

The relative regional importance of the various types of livestock is primarily related to the availability of fodder, and therefore to crop-geography. The markets for animal products are restricted by the poverty of most Spaniards, and only near the largest and wealthiest cities can real dairy farming and stock fattening develop. In rainier areas fodder is obtainable the year round either from arable land or from natural pasture, except in the mountain regions where some vertical transhumance is still practised. Here, therefore, cattle for work, meat and milk, swine for meat and sheep for wool all have their place. In the 'huerta' regions land usable for high value cash crops is generally too scarce for fodder production, and sheep, goats and swine find subsistence on the arid margins. On the great 'secano' lands of the Meseta and the Ebro basin, fodder grain can only be safely spared for work animals, and the stubble and wasteland come into their own for feeding goats and sheep.

This threefold division of Spain conceals many detailed variations; but for crops, livestock and even rural society it has some significance. Spain is still primarily a country of farmers, with 50% of an active male population of over nine millions still engaged in agriculture. (Compare Turkey 66%, Italy 41%, U.K. 6%.) Farm products still make up 55% of total exports even though they also compose one-third of the imports. Spain produces *c.* 40% of the world output of olive oil.

This rural population has a historical background that leads to a distrust of finance and of land improvement. Quantity has always appeared more important than quality in a country where security was rare. The absence of commercial opportunity and good communications has encouraged parochialism, even in relatively safer days. The historic growth of large estates, short leases, and their concomitant class of poor landless labourers in Andalusia, Ávila and other central and southern provinces has discouraged peasant initiative—although much has been and still is being done to correct this social mal-factor. Lack of security, gross inequality of land ownership and the need for fallowing that almost verges on shifting cultivation have all combined to encourage a nucleation of rural settlement that in itself causes much waste of effort and obstruction of technical progress. On the most fertile lands, those of the 'huertas' and of Galicia, population growth largely unrelieved by alternative employment has over-strained resources, and by producing small-scale though intensive farming has also produced an obstruction to change and development. Superficially there is much technical backwardness. Spanish agriculture is one of the least mechanised in Europe, and both where suitable and where not, the cultivator must largely rely on his own manual labour and rule-of-thumb experience.

We may leave the agricultural landscape with one last analogy between the lands of a Galician village and Spain itself. The village classification of land is of 'Vegas', 'Mesetas', 'Eriales'—fertile lowlands, dry slopes and terrace-lands, and wooded waste. So in Spain there are the fertile rainy and irrigated lowlands of mixed crops, the Meseta and Ebro basin of dry-farmed grain and sheep, and the wastelands of high mountains and barren limestone. The last two zones are immeasurably the greater—the total perennially irrigated area covers about 9 million acres, and the rainy lowlands about 2 million, out of a total area of over 125 million acres. The surprising fact is not that Spanish agriculture is so inefficient but that it is so productive—average grain yields region for region compare favourably with environmental analogues elsewhere, and national averages are close to those of the U.S.A. and U.S.S.R.

MINES, POWER AND MANUFACTURES

Extractive industry in Spain is almost wholly confined to four highland regions, the Cantabrians, Sierra Morena, Sierra Nevada and the southern Iberian mountains and their continuation into the Catalan hills. The Tertiary basins of the Castiles and the Ebro basin, and the granite-lands (which with the exception of Galicia have a low agricultural capacity), have little mineral wealth.

For the internal economy of the country coal production (which reached 15 million tons in 1960) is the most important. The best bituminous coals are obtained from Carboniferous beds, and the Asturian field around Oviedo produces about 75% of the total. Isolated basins on the southern flanks of the Cantabrians, mainly in the province of León, produce another 10% of bituminous coal and most of the national anthracite total of just over a million tons. The other coalfields are small and scattered, in Ciudad Real; Córdoba and Extramadura; in the northern Iberian mountains; the central Pyrenees; and the Catalan hills.

Most Spanish coal is friable and of inferior quality, and generally unsuitable for metallurgical coke-making. It still finds its main market in the railways (although electrification of main lines is proceeding rapidly), and in the tariff-protected iron and steel industry. The coalfields away from the Asturias

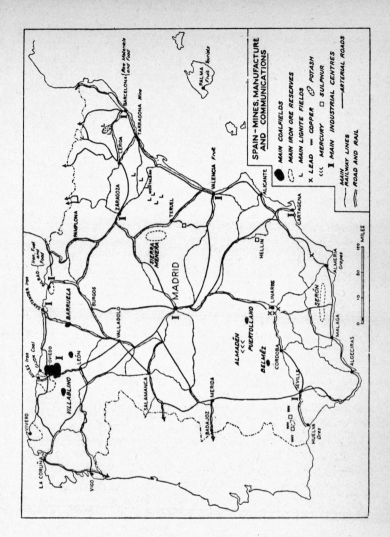

12 Mines,
Manufactures
and Com-
munications

are of importance mainly for supplying the fuel-starved centre
—particularly Madrid.

Iron ore of varying grades and quantities is to be found
everywhere other than in the Tertiary areas. The best carbon-
ate ores of the Vizcaya region and the hematite ores of Santander are approaching exhaustion, and the Basque iron and
steel industry is having to turn to other and lower grade supplies. The quantitatively most important reserves are high-
silica ores of Asturias and Galicia; the latter being particularly
intractable.

Potentially more important although remote from fuel supplies are the dolomitic ores of the Sierra Menera in the
Iberian mountains, and the hematites of Granada. Their real
value is reduced by relative inaccessibility and the lack of
fuel.

Lead, copper and mercury mining have all been important
throughout history. Lead blende is now mainly extracted in the
eastern Sierra Morena around the mining and smelting town
of Linares. Copper pyrites are also products of the Sierra
Morena, chiefly of the Rio Tinto region. The port of Huelva
handles most of the copper and pyrites for export. Mercury,
of which Spain is the world's chief supplier, has retained its
historic importance and Almadén still has vast reserves. The
sulphur of Albacete and Teruel is in much the same case.

Potentially more important than all the vein minerals are
the vast potash deposits of the Cardoner valley in Catalonia.
To be ranked with the major known reserves of the world,
their present production of some 5% of the global total in no
way indicates their real value.

The distribution of solid fuel reserves and of mineral deposits
indicates the nature of the economic problems that confront
Spain. The most needed resources for full-scale industrialisation are for the most part inadequate in quantity, difficult to
extract and to utilise, and above all scattered. The costs of
extraction and transportation are high, the communication
network insufficiently developed, therefore concentration is
difficult. The utilisation of common and potassic salts, bauxite
and sulphur, in chemical and other light industries, requires

an industrial and technical background which Spain is still acquiring.

The exploitation of water power has made great strides in recent years. Direct use is now unimportant except in upland Catalonia, but hydro-electricity first installed on a large scale at Madrid in 1898 now composes 80% of all electricity produced. Generating capacity was doubled between 1926 and 1936 and again between 1939 and 1953. The main potential lies in the rainy north—roughly 50% in the Ebro catchment basin and 25% in the Cantabrians. The streams have steep gradients, large volumes and in most years the summer period of low water is short. The Cinca-Segre basin has become preeminent because here the catchment basin is sufficiently large to allow the development of big generating stations, and industrial Catalonia offers an eager market for power. In arid Spain, topographical conditions are good but fluctuations in river volume extreme. Power generation therefore calls for heavy capital investment in artificially dammed reservoirs, and in most summers capacity cannot be fully utilised. The National Gas, Water and Electricity Council estimated in 1963 that net output of hydro-electricity fluctuated between 48,000 KWh in an average year and 40,000 KWh in a dry year.

Manufacturing industry as a whole is obviously in difficulties. Fuel and power are short, raw materials and fuel have to be imported and paid for by a restricted number of surplus agricultural commodities, and the internal shortage of capital and markets further obstructs development. In general it is true that, except in Vascongadas and Catalonia, social and geographical factors have combined to hamper the growth of manufacture.

Industrial employees form 22% of the total occupied labour force, the main groups in order of importance being in iron and steel, textiles, woodworking and food processing. The whole chemical industry employs only about 60,000 workers. Traditional industries of local importance are to be found in every town but large-scale factory manufacture is extremely localised. Catalonia has 50% of the chemical industries, and over 80% of the cotton, rayon and wool working capacity. Of the 2 million tons of steel now produced annually Vizcaya produces some 80%, and in the same region are situated two out of the three shipyards capable of constructing large vessels. In 1963, a record year, 77,000 automobiles and 56,100 commercial vehicles were produced, mainly at Barcelona.

Spain is caught in a vicious cycle. Even at a low level of consumption the annual fuel deficit is about one million tons of coal or coal equivalent. Without more fuel metallurgical production cannot expand, and the vast need for capital goods remains unsatisfied. Without such capital goods, in particular transport equipment, general productivity cannot be raised. Low productivity restricts internal markets, and low internal purchasing power makes manufacturing runs short and of high cost. The high costs of exports of processed goods make it difficult for Spain to supplement resource deficiencies by importation.

The greatest shortage is of capital. The agrarian sector of the economy is both unable and unwilling to invest much savings outside farming. Until recent years, foreign capital was viewed with suspicion; but by now, more than 50% of the capital of any enterprise may be held abroad. Some of the reasons for these attitudes will appear in the chapters on historical geography. In spite of it all, however, Spain is moving, and industrial production as a whole has increased by more than 50% since 1937–39.

COMMUNICATIONS, PORTS AND TRADE

Transportation is now developing. Spain possesses much terrain that is difficult and expensive to negotiate by road or rail, and all the peripheral regions are separated by such obstacles from the interior and often from each other. More important is the effect on costs of the vast tracts of relatively negative land that lie between the various centres. Traffic originating at any of the major peripheral regions has to bear virtually the whole cost of the communication system to the final destination since local traffic is slight. Even so the national rail network (Renfe) loses between £5 and £8 million sterling a year. The same difficulties arise here that beset manufacturing industry. Greater demand for transport cannot appear until local self-sufficiency decreases and more integrated use is made of resources. Better communications are in turn necessary for breaking down regionalism and a parochial outlook: but capital and resources for such a long-term policy are scarce.

The ports of Spain fall into clearly defined groups. Four of the five leading exporters (by tonnage) send out mining products and take in general merchandise and foodstuffs. Huelva, the most important of these, is entirely dependent on the metals extracted in the western Sierra Morena, since it has an otherwise poor hinterland and practically no industries. Gijón, its outport of Musel, and Avilés export mainly by coastal shipping, coal from Oviedo and agricultural produce of the Asturian littoral. Imports are of iron, fuel and food, almost entirely for the Oviedo industrial region; and mixed industries have developed on the basis of this exchange. Bilbao, the third biggest exporter, is in a different class from the others in that it is second only to Barcelona for imports and because it is a manufacturing centre in its own right. Exports are mainly of iron ore and metals to points abroad, with imports of fuels for local industry and general supplies for the dense population of industrial Vascongadas.

Of the main importing centres, Barcelona is by far the greatest. As the port for the chief industrial region of Spain it ranks in Europe with Bordeaux for total tonnage handled, and in value its trade is almost three times as great as that of Bilbao. The fact that 80% of its trade consists of imports is explained both by their nature—raw materials, machinery, fuel, foodstuffs for industrial Catalonia—and by the fact that most of the regionally manufactured goods move into Spain rather than are exported. It is in its own right the chief manufacturing town as well as having the full range of port activities. Unlike the other centres so far mentioned, Barcelona has no natural coastal inlet and considerable artificial works have been necessary.

The remaining ports may be classified as follows. First there are the Mediterranean and southern ports dealing in the main with exports of agricultural produce and imports of manufactured goods, fuel, fertilisers and timber. This traditional function is performed to the virtual exclusion of other urban activities. Valencia, the most important, alone possesses much manufacturing industry, and even this is overwhelmingly concerned with the processing of farm produce. The sites of all the Mediterranean ports are of interest because longshore movement that may cause silting up has had obvious effects on their fortunes. Málaga is sited east of an estuary. Farther northward at Almeria and Tarragona, safety lies to the west of the river-mouths.

Secondly come the Atlantic ports handling big ships and small coastal vessels. Vigo, and less important La Coruña, come into this category, each with good deepwater ria harbours. Exports are small and are mainly coastal, imports and passengers are largely derived from transatlantic trade. Their economic importance is less to Galicia than to Madrid.

Thirdly are the naval arsenals, one El Ferrol on a good ria harbour in Atlantic Galicia, the second, Cartagena with an equally good landlocked natural harbour in the Mediterranean. Cartagena much more than its rival has some normal commercial life and industrial development—mainly of silver and lead refining—but this is overshadowed by naval activities.

Trade, as appears from this brief analysis of ports, is both regionally specialised and nationally restricted. The necessary import of raw materials, fuel and foodstuffs as well as manufactures is characteristic of poor or undeveloped countries. Exports of Mediterranean farm produce and a decreasing quantity of raw minerals and concentrates which local industry cannot handle are insufficient to balance the import bill. Even with low internal consumption rates there is therefore a normal trade deficit. The United States is Spain's most important supplier and West Germany is the most important customer. Other principal suppliers are the U.K. and France; the U.K., Italy, and France are leading customers.

In this brief statement much must be left unsaid. The main characteristics of Spain's economic geography, however, may be outlined as follows. Agricultural productivity is low over most of the country mainly because of environmental difficulty. The removal of social and technical obstructions would produce a slight but sufficient improvement, sufficient, that is, to enable Spain to build up a positive trade balance. This in turn would make possible concentration on imports of capital goods with which resource-utilisation could be intensified and wealth increased.

As in the case of other relatively undeveloped countries Spain cannot afford to import agricultural products as well as capital equipment for her industries. The precarious nature of her economic balance is illustrated by the fact that in some years—in 1956–57, for example—the olive and wheat crops have supplied only three-quarters of domestic demand. Citrus exports also vary considerably. Much can be blamed on hazardous environment; equally, much of the danger arises from technical and social backwardness. As discussed in Chapter VI and the regional sections, Spain has been left a legacy of parochialism and sectionalism, and the many virtues of peasant independence and industrial and political syndicalism are strongly tinged both with conservatism and with anarchy. To this fundamental proposition each analytical approach tends to return.

Since 1960, however, the outlook has become brighter. The average economic growth rate has jumped to some 5% per year. By 1962 Spanish gold and foreign exchange reserves had soared to around $1 billion from virtually nil a decade before. The great agricultural resettlement schemes in Badajoz and Jaén have begun to pay off, industrial production is now running at more than twice the volume of 1950, and national income per capita has risen by 50% in the same period. In absolute terms Spain still has a long way to go, and local and regional poverty is not uncommon, but Spanish ability and resilience together with U.S. aid and Franco-German investment are producing a transformation of real significance.

Chapter 8

CULTURAL ASPECTS

THE feature of strong national unity derived from and transcending regional individuality, so marked in France, does not exist in Spain. Instead there are several Spains—not only geographical and historical, but also in culture.

LANGUAGE

Underlying much of the cultural diversity is an important variation in language. Three quite distinctive linguistic forms are still current as everyday speech: Basque, Castilian and Catalan, whilst the latter two also have within them significantly different regional dialects, which unmistakably stamp their users. Some of these dialects represent further ancient languages which have become degraded and are in process of assimilation.

The Basques. The Basque language (Euskera) is spoken by over half a million Spaniards in the corner adjacent to the south-west frontier of France, comprising the modern province of Guipuzcoa and parts of Vizcaya, Alava and Navarre. At one time, to judge by the distribution of place-names, Basque was spoken in most of the central and western Pyrenees, together with parts of the Cantabrians. In Roman times the Vascones who have given their name to both Biscay and Gascony, and who could probably be equated with the Basques, were certainly more widespread.

Within Spain, Castilian Spanish has gradually replaced Basque, a process greatly hastened during the last century and a half by the industrialisation of the towns, and development of sea communications—e.g. Bilbao was once Basque-speaking, but is hardly so any longer. The Basque language is of exceptional difficulty and complexity,[1] and many sub-dialects (as many as 25 or 30) are said to occur, even at present.

The Basques still preserve a strong sense of family, amounting almost to a patriarchal system, in which the head of the household exacts respect, but is almost himself in duty bound to ensure the welfare of all members: a livelihood for the men, and dowries for the girls.

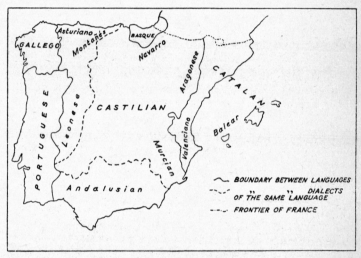

13 Language Distribution

The Basques have a somewhat distinctive appearance, being moderate or short in stature (5 ft. 4 ins. to 5 ft. 5 ins.), and rather spare physique, with broader shoulders and narrow hips. Facial features are small and often dominated by a straight nose and well-developed forehead. In head-form the Basques tend to be neither particularly round- nor particularly broad-headed (i.e. mesacephalic), with an average cephalic index of 78. A further point of difference is that the

[1] It is said locally that the Devil, as a punishment for some outrageous offence, was condemned to learn Basque as a penance.

Basques are slightly fairer than the other populations of Spain, who are generally dark.[1]

The Basques have a developed national sense; and demands for 'home rule' in Basque territories have been put forward. One tangible result is that street and place-names are usually given in both Spanish and Basque in the towns. They have annual gatherings of a social and ceremonial kind, somewhat reminiscent of an 'Eisteddfod', often on sites where there are oak-groves.[2] The Basques have given to the world a game, *pelota*, possibly the ancestor of fives and tennis; a form of head-wear, the *beret*; and at least one Saint—Ignatius Loyola, the founder of the Jesuit Order.

Castilian. Castilian is spoken as a first language by about 20 millions of the inhabitants of Spain, and is unquestionably the dominant form of Spanish in the peninsula—few are totally ignorant of it. Since 1250 it has been the official language of government. Originally the native speech (derived from Latin) of the northern kingdoms round Santander which avoided dominance by the Moors, Castilian spread southwards with the Reconquista, and became in effect the principal language of the Meseta.

In its spread, it absorbed a number of equally ancient (and related) forms of speech: Leonese, once a language in its own right, with a copious early literature, and current in the old Kingdom of León; and Aragonese, again an old language associated with a territorial unit. Both Leonese and Aragonese are now as it were degraded to local dialects, with distinctive forms surviving in a few places. Leonese survivals occur in the provinces of Zamora (the Maragato dialect) and Salamanca, with two other forms (Asturiano and Montañés) current in the Cantabrian uplands. Aragonese is still spoken in a few higher

[1] There is much interest in the extent to which racial differences would appear to be indicated by variation in blood grouping. This relationship would seem to be particularly clear within Iberia, especially for the Basques. Unfortunately, the topic is too extensive for treatment here.

[2] The town of Guernica is a centre; and the famous oak-grove there was destroyed by German dive-bombers during the Civil War.

valleys of the Pyrenees, and a mixture with French is the dialect of Navarre (Navarro).

Besides these amalgamations with formerly distinctive languages, there are various regional dialects of Castilian which indicate district of origin even more clearly than, say, the local speech of various parts of New England or the American South. Andalusian, Extramaduran and Murcian forms of Castilian are strongly developed, with marked individuality in pronunciation, syntax and vocabulary.

Castilian has also been influenced to a slight degree by Arabic, in vocabulary only, not in grammar. As might be expected the farther south one goes, the greater the number of Arab words in use. Incidentally, the cultural influence of the Arabs is much clearer in the music of southern Spain—one has only to hear recordings of 'Flamenco' music to appreciate the closeness to Arab styles.

Catalan. This language, by reason of its structure, wide distribution and extensive early and modern literature, which put it clearly as a definite stage between Castilian, Italian and Provençal, must also be considered as a separate language. At present, Catalan is spoken by 6–7 million people, including a number of French living in Roussillon; over 100,000 emigrants in the New World; and the inhabitants of Alghero, a town in Sardinia. Catalan is very far from being a mere antique now in process of extinction, though it is also clear that it was once much more widespread than at the present day, even reaching the mainland of Italy. Three dialects can be recognised, Catalan proper, spoken round Barcelona; Valenciano; and Balear, with distinctive variations even between the Balearic islands.

Like Basque, but to an even greater degree, the Catalan language has undergone considerable revival over the last century and a half, paralleled by a strong separatist and regionalist movement. Portugal just succeeded in establishing permanent independence of Madrid: the Catalonian provinces just failed. There was a sustained attempt to separate during the Thirty Years War; and a century of agitation after

1810 succeeded in bringing the government of Spain to agree in 1914 to the establishment of a Mancomunidad, or Catalan administration, which handled certain governmental functions in the four provinces of Barcelona, Tarragona, Lérida and Gerona. An echo of President Wilson's Armistice proposals on self-determination for oppressed national groups led to a demand for fuller autonomy, which was also taken up by the Basque provinces and Galicia—but the problem was shelved by the time-honoured device of appointing a Government Commission to investigate.

In 1923, following a military *coup d'état*, the Mancomunidad was abolished, without much reaction in Catalonia. However, separatism revived under the Republic, and was both a source of strength and a thorn in the side of the Republican government. Being partly industrialised, the temper of Catalonia was definitely Republican and 'left wing'; but claims for autonomy that were put forward weakened the Republic's rule as a whole. Under General Franco there have been no concessions to Catalan separatism, but there have been sporadic 'strikes' in Catalonia, ostensibly over such matters as bus fares, but possibly with a more political design.

The opponents of Catalan separatism deride its aims, some of which are extravagant (e.g. the creation of a pan-Catalan state in the Western Mediterranean to include Sardinia and Sicily), and accuse its sponsors of being a factious clique of professional political agitators, disgruntled intellectuals, and self-seeking business men without any real backing from the mass of the Catalan populations. The real aims of Catalan separatism, it is argued, can be summed in the words 'autonomia con subvención'—political freedom but with subsidies from Madrid.

Galician. Gallego, the language of Galicia, is spoken by about 2½ million people, and is virtually the same as Portuguese. Its distribution is confined to the four provinces of Galicia, together with a small fringe on the north-west edge of the Meseta. Unlike Catalan and Basque, Gallego has no considerable literature, and it tends now to survive only as a rural dialect, having largely disappeared from the towns. Although attempts have been made to revive it, these have been on the whole distinctly less successful than in Catalonia and the Basque provinces.

RELIGION

The outstanding characteristic of the Spanish people has been its uncompromising attachment to the Roman Church, even from a period as early as that of the Visigoths. We have observed the attitudes developed over eight centuries of religious crusading, culminating in the expulsion of Moors and Jews, and the maintenance of strict Catholic orthodoxy through the activities of the Inquisition. Today, as a result, there are no significant religious minorities. Protestants number about 20,000, and for the majority of Spaniards the only choice lies between official Catholicism or private free-thinking. Old attitudes still persist. It is illegal to print and circulate the Protestant Bible, and within recent years there have been several physical attacks by mobs on Protestant meeting-houses. Moreover, a Spanish archbishop in 1955 was publicly censured by the Pope for intolerance and a reactionary outlook.

This often obscurantist attitude has tended to keep Spain out of many intellectual advances, a large proportion of which since 1600 have come from Protestant nations. Ayala suggests that many elements in modern capitalist development (and hence in technology) were provoked by the influence of the Reformation—and Spain's violent rejection of the one cut her off from the other. Instead, Spain was driven back to reaction and the impossible task of trying to maintain orthodoxy by authoritarian means. Progressive and liberal opinions could not make themselves felt—instead, Spain has swung between the extremes of despotism and syndicalism.

This lack, or failure to develop a real 'middle way', has had a profound effect on Spanish culture in general. There has been willingness to recognise and explore to the full the wide variety in human life—but most attention has been given to extremes, from the extravagances of romantic idealised chivalry in the Middle Ages to the realism, often sordid, of contemporary everyday life. This is especially well seen in Spanish painting. The three greatest native artists, Velasquez, Murillo and Goya, all achieved recognition first as Court painters, but each had another side. Velasquez had a predilection for humble interiors, Murillo developed a 'mentality of the back street' and Goya turned his portraits of aristocratic patrons into savage caricatures.

LITERATURE

Similarly in Spanish literature there is oscillation and vacillation from opposing points of view. The mediaeval figure of El Cid is treated in the *Poema de Mio Cid* as grave, wise and statesmanlike; but in other ballads, he is wild, headstrong and insolent. The French version of the same poems is on the other hand quite consistent. Lope de Vega, the greatest Spanish playwright (contemporary with Shakespeare), refused to distinguish between high tragedy and comedy, but employed both together. Similarly, can one call *Don Quixote* a humorous or a tragic story?

One of the earliest forms in Spanish literature were the epics or *cantares de gesta*. These took as themes (*a*) the Christian struggle against the Moors, (*b*) the rivalry of the feudal Christian states, or (*c*) legends of Carolingian and Visigothic times, roughly comparable with the Arthurian legends of England and France. Alongside these were lyrical poems concerned with nature and human love. The performers or reciters of epics on the whole were Castilians, the poems were more often in Gallego; and, whilst the greater part of the inspiration was purely native, there was some influence by French (especially southern French) models.

The expansion of Spain in the 15th and 16th centuries was a great stimulus to literature, and these two periods are spoken of as the Golden Age of Spanish literature. Achievement of internal union, so closely followed by the complete triumph of the Reconquista, was continued by Spanish occupation of the Americas, and the political supremacy of Spain in Europe. The Crusading ideal seemed to have brilliantly justified itself; and Spanish writers undertook to codify, explain, comment upon and expand the political and cultural achievements of their country. University reform, with emphasis on a national outlook rather than the internationalism characteristic of the Middle Ages, helped to raise Castilian to parity with Latin as a language in its own right.

Spanish writers showed most early activity in lyric poetry, in which they were at first influenced by Italy, the home of the Renaissance; and in theology, especially mysticism. Later, the voyages and ideas of the great explorers and missionaries were congenial, epic subjects. Columbus, Vasco da Gama, Balboa and Cortés left reports and documents which formed the basis of biographies and geographical treatises. There is even a disquisition on the humanitarian aspects of employing the subject Arawaks of the West Indies in forced labour.

Another, partly related field was that of the prose narrative or novel, which ultimately produced its finest expression in *Don Quixote* by Cervantes (1547–1616). One element in many novels of this period was adventure and travel in strange new lands, with personal prowess and eager uninhibited characters. Towards the end of the 16th century, however, this bright extrovert adventurousness had shaded off into doubt, introspection and disillusion, with tragedy breaking through to leaven humour and inhibit attainment of the ideal. Moreover, optimism became increasingly tinged by realism, the portrayal of which greatly preoccupied the later writers of the Golden Age.

These are the elements woven together in *Don Quixote*: generous and romantic idealism tempered by cold realisation of the world as it actually is (Cervantes was for a time a galley-slave), with the incidental comicalities of day-to-day existence rounded by the final tragedy of failure.

Pursuit of true realism in everyday affairs led to frank interest in low life, from which grew an especially Spanish literary form, the picaresque novel, or story of seedy, dubious characters. The 'heroes' are comic and ingenious rogues, whose greatest tragedy befalls when they are faced with making an honest living. Some are the servants of gullible masters, some university students—portrayed in a manner that recalls Chaucer—some are, one might say, vagabonds in their own right. From the picaresque novels can be traced a number of 'stock' figures in later international literature and music— Figaro, Gil Blas, Don Juan, and possibly in spirit only the creations of Damon Runyon.

The last period of the *Siglo de Oro* was dominated by two playwrights: Lope de Vega and Calderón. The former was almost incredibly prolific. Besides poems and novels, over 700 plays are known (and some ascribe a further 1100 to him) —nearly all of good quality and many of the highest order. Calderón is reputed as the writer of philosophical and religious themes (his best known play is *Life is a Dream*) and he greatly influenced later Romantic writers, especially in England and Germany.

After the death of Calderón in 1681, Spanish literature underwent a marked decline. The 18th century is mainly noteworthy for the lack of native Spanish ideas, owing to dominance of French thought, which came in with the Bourbon monarchy in 1700; and also for the emergence of local regional 'schools' of literature, in Salamanca and Seville particularly.

The Romantic movement of the early 19th century provoked sympathetic response in Spain, heightened by the death in 1833 of the anti-Liberal Ferdinand VII. It is remarkable that the greatest single influence on the Spanish Romantics seems to have been Walter Scott; and Spanish Romantics turned to the re-discovery of their own Golden Age writers, and to the portrayal of local colour, especially from the Orient and from their own Islamic past, with more than a due emphasis on the tragic, gloomy and ugly aspects of life. Disillusion again could be said to be the keynote.

Since the Romantic period, regionalism and characterisation have been prominent in Spanish literature. Blasco Ibañez (1867–1928) first achieved recognition by his stories of Valencian peasant life (e.g. *La Barraca*) set round Valencia and the

Albufera. He later passed to wider, epic themes (*Blood and Sand*, *The Four Horseman of the Apocalypse*) that have earned for him the scorn of literary critics, and the respect of Metro-Goldwyn-Mayer. Most evolved of the 'regional' groups is the Catalan school, which by its volume of output and use of Catalan as distinct from Castilian Spanish might almost be regarded as a separate movement.

Spanish philosophers and essayists (Ortega y Gasset, 'Azorin' [Ruiz], Unamuno, and de Madariaga) have an international reputation at the present time. Hence, although Spanish literature could hardly be said to have a sustained and progressive development over the centuries, with the power of exerting consistent influence on that of other countries, it nevertheless has qualities of its own, which in some ways reflect those of Spain herself. As geographical environment shows little regularity or order, with fairly abrupt changes from the opulent to the barren, so Spanish literature possesses its excellencies and also its sterilities. Furthermore, if a parallel can be drawn between the garden-like landscape of France and its well-ordered, balanced literature, then equally it would seem the rugged unevenness of Spain—embodying the harsh, the crude, the sensuous and the brilliant with an underlying vitality—all this finds an echo in the works of its writers.

CONTEMPORARY SPANISH LIFE

Daily Life. 'The attention of commanding officers', ran one of Lord Wellington's orders during his Spanish campaign, 'has been frequently called to the expediency of supplying the soldiers with breakfast.' This might well be taken as an indirect commentary on conditions in many parts of Spain. Frugal living, with two, but not always three daily meals, is common; and the mainstays of diet are cereals, vegetables and fruit. Meat is really a luxury, and milk scarce, except in humid Spain.

Natural conditions impose certain strong controls upon the range of foodstuffs. Dairy and animal produce tend to be lacking except in the favoured north-west; and poor communications impose self-sufficiency, with bread as the staple article of diet. Unlike Italy, where the hard winter wheats make poor bread but excellent pastas such as macaroni and spaghetti, Spain is a nation of bread eaters, though pastas are also much used, especially in the east and south—wheat for choice, but adulterated with maize, barley or rye if necessary. Animal fat is scarce, hence olive, or (increasingly in the south-east) peanut oil take its place. Meat is used sparingly, in sausage form, or merely as a flavouring rather than a basis. Strongly flavoured vegetables—the onion, artichoke, pepper or tomato—often provide the principal relish in an otherwise monotonous farinaceous diet. Wine is the everyday beverage, with, like France, a cider region in the north-west.

The Family. The state is often ineffective, and general social consciousness is little developed, hence the chief social unit in Spain is the family. Parents still play a considerable part in the lives of their children: marriages are to a considerable degree legal arrangements between families—'alliances' in the fuller sense of the word, with the dowry playing an indispensable part. Betrothal can sometimes occur during childhood, and the young couple involved may have very little voice in these arrangements. But the Spanish family is at least as stable as in Britain or America, and the proportion of broken marriages is far smaller.

There is something of a paradox in the position of women. In many ways, they have a subordinate and inferior position, especially in the south of Spain. Here, where perhaps Mohammadan ideas still linger most strongly, girls of middle- and upper-class families are expected to stay indoors, and in fact rarely leave the house unescorted by a male relative. They may not receive much formal education: in 1933, out of 1200 students at the University of Murcia, only 28 were women. Among the poorer classes, women tend to be drudges, and responsible for what many in this country would regard as more than a strict share of family duties.

In consequence, women play a restricted part in society and

general social activities. There are two somewhat contrasting sides to Spanish life—the family circle, to which outsiders are not readily admitted, and social intercourse in public, which centres on the main square (plaza), with its cafés and opportunities for promenading.

Yet the masculinity of Spanish society, pronounced though this is, could not be said to be complete. One significant feature is that customarily a man will call himself formally by the family names of both parents (unless he is a Basque, when he will often use the name of a district, or a house). The maternal name is added last, giving a combination that is not at first easily recognised: e.g. Miguel Cervantes de Saavedra, Diego Velasquez de Silva. Also, the so-called 'Salic Law', (excluding queens from ruling in their own right), has never fully operated in Spain, even in the Bourbon monarchy.

Temperament. The Spaniard is a strongly convinced individualist; the person to him being far more important than any institution or political organisation. Castilians formally accepted their monarch in the words 'We who are as good as you', and modern syndicalist anarchist views seem to have found a hold in Spain stronger than anywhere else in Western Europe. Even present-day matadors, proceeding together towards the President's box at the start of a bull-fight, are careful not to march in step.

Buttressing the individualist outlook is a strong sense of pride and personal dignity. Cervantes mentions the often-cited instance of the nobleman in reduced circumstances who starved rather than undertake a lower-class occupation: there is the more authentic attitude of the hungry inhabitants of Zaragoza, besieged in 1809, who contemptuously returned loaves of bread thrown over the walls by the French army. This attitude has several interesting implications. If every individual is to be taken at his own evaluation of himself, the only feasible social approach is one of complete equality. This surprising practical result is shown in the way social egalitarianism is carried on in public—e.g. in small cafés, where every new arrival is greeted by a word from every table, and is expected to reply; or in trains, where easy mixing of various conditions of passengers is a striking feature.

On the other hand, an individualist basis for social relations implies a mistrust or indifference to public institutions, political and financial. As compared with the Anglo-Saxon world, there are few charitable foundations, or benevolent institutions, and little disposition to apply general criteria to behaviour. Instead, charity is personal, from one to another, and human relations tend to be governed by sentiment. 'I will do this for you personally' is a stronger motivating force than 'It is my duty to act'.

Similarly, a refusal to accept general, impersonal values can lead to much difficulty in the political sphere. Maintenance of relations on a personal footing tends to engender a mistrust of government and the state. In one's dealings with the state, a lower standard of conduct can therefore be tolerated— sometimes mere indifference, shading into abuses such as nepotism or financial corruption.

Opposed to this attitude are occasional remarkable demonstrations of the willingness of Spaniards to tolerate authority. Most impressive is the ready acceptance of religious dogma. It is fair to say that Spain is more 'religious' than either France or Italy—at least, religion sits more lightly on both the latter countries. Moreover, though originally developed elsewhere, the Inquisition found its most congenial territory in Spain, and came ultimately to be regarded as typically Spanish. In minor matters two small instances may be noted. It has been observed that the Madrileños, in many respects traditionally unruly, obey strict traffic and pedestrian rules far more punctiliously than even Germans or British. The clothing rules regarding shirt-sleeves in public and the style of bathing costumes are also peculiar to Spain.

The personal temper of the people, together with lack of geographical unity within the Peninsula, have produced a recurrent situation of political unbalance and instability. Regional particularism has not so far completely achieved the transition from a provincial to a national scale. In the view of some modern Spaniards who have written on this topic,

Spain remains incomplete as a nation. The diversities listed in this volume—in topography, ways of living and culture—have so far prevented the emergence of a single coherent political unit. As a result, Spain in the modern world is an anachronism, a third-rate power, from which little can be expected in the future.

This view, however, is contestable. Given even short periods of relative stability and quiet, Spanish life has shown itself to have much underlying vitality, and to be capable of progress. Economically, developments of a significant kind have taken place since the end of the Civil War; and in earlier chapters the argument is developed that Spanish agriculture is a successful use of an extraordinarily difficult environment rather than a slovenly use of good terrain. The Spanish cereal farmer gets as much from his land as do his counterparts in the U.S.A. and U.S.S.R.

In the political sphere, it is worth recalling that an appraisal of Spanish potential in 1940 gave even Hitler pause—*guerrilla* is a Spanish word: and though specifically condemned by a resolution of United Nations, the authoritarian régime of General Franco has remained as the only one of its kind to outlast the Second War. At least the Caudillo can say, with Sieyès, 'J'ai survecu'. There is also on record a resolution of certain U.S. Senators that Spain by its geography and political evolution represents the safest and most dependable ally in Europe.

The unexpected resiliency of Spanish institutions has of recent years led some Spaniards to suggest that in the future Spain may have an enhanced rôle to play in world affairs. Of moderate, but not large size, and therefore no longer to be feared militarily; without racial feeling; connected closely by culture to Latin America, and less distinctly, but perceptibly to the Arab world, Spain may yet become one of the influential 'third forces' of the future. Very lack of material success may, paradoxically, once again prove to be a source of political advantage in the modern world.

Part III

REGIONAL GEOGRAPHY

Chapter 9

NORTHERN SPAIN

NORTH of the Sierra Morena and north-west of the Valencian coastlands lies a great mass of Continental and Atlantic Spain together with the narrow fringe of Mediterranean Catalonia.

This area has little obvious homogeneity; indeed the Meseta heart of Spain has always found the old saying to be true: 'Two mules one may drive, three will tear you asunder'. Nevertheless, northern Spain does have a certain unity. This is partly because regional feelings tend to cancel each other out, partly because no single one of the peripheral regions has been sufficiently well endowed successfully to break away, but mainly because of the common tradition of the Reconquista. Indeed, Castile whose dominance produces such regional restiveness, may be regarded as an intensely concentrated projection of all the characteristics of those same regions, of the Ebro, of Asturias, of La Mancha and Galicia, of all that is Spanish.

Northern Spain is Spanish Spain, that area least affected by the incursion of Islamic Africa, and its limits are approximately those reached by the Christian kingdoms before the last great surge of 13th-century reconquest.

By the early 13th century the Moslems had been pushed back to those regions in which their culture, economy and society had become most firmly rooted. In Andalusia, Murcia and Valencia lay the garden lands of the vine and citrus fruit, the date-palm and the mulberry. With some justification it was held that the Islamic Paradise was suspended over Málaga. Ethnically, culturally, and everywhere in the landscape they left their impress.

In contrast the Moslems but lightly touched the less amenable central and northern lands. In the Ebro basin it is true they established the 'huerta' kingdoms of Zaragoza and Lérida, but these isolated outliers were finally overwhelmed only the more completely by reason of their exotic character. The legacy of Islam survives still in northern Spain—the lateen sail along the Asturian coast, the 'shadouf' well in Orense and Cuenca, urban architecture, dialect loanwords,—but it appears poor when compared with that in the south. Northern Spain is now undeniably part of Europe.

The territory of Spain is here treated in twenty-two regional studies grouped as detailed below and illustrated by five regional maps, Figs. 14–18. The 'rationale' of the grouping is derived in the main from the historical evolution of the human societies settled in each region.

I. The North-West—León and Castile
    A. Galicia
    B. Asturias
    C. The Threshold of León
    D. Old Castile

II. The North-East—Navarre and Aragón
    A. Navarre
    B. The Pyrenees
    C. The Ebro Basin
    D. The Iberian Mountains
    E. Catalonia—The Hills
               —The Coastlands

III. Central Spain—The Meseta
    A. The Central Sierras
    B. New Castile
    C. La Mancha
    D. The Threshold of Júcar

Chapter 10

THE NORTH-WEST

GALICIA is a structural old-land. West of a line running south from Ribadeo to the Sil river lie granites, schists and slates, little affected by the folding so marked in the Cantabrians, but considerably faulted and tilted during the Alpine orogenesis.

The coastlines in general and in detail are largely controlled by the systems of faults running in two directions. West–east lines of weakness determine the alignment of the Rias Bajas, and produce inland the depressions of the rivers Miño, Lerez and Ulla. Crossing this latitudinal arrangement almost at right angles are north–south running fault-zones, one of which determines the main western coastline. From the human point of view, however, the most important fault-line is the Tuy–Padrón–Portomouro rift. Farther to the east, and associated with Hercynian tectonic movement, lies the great belt of schists stretching south from Vivero to Monforte de Lemos.

In the main then Galicia, as also northern Portugal, is to be considered as a grid-faulted granitic block with schist inliers and a few small Tertiary basins such as that of Monforte.

On this comparatively stable block, pre-Tertiary drainage systems produced a mature, undulating topography, of the type associated with old igneous rock weathering. Later tectonic action finally resulted in the elevation of this old peneplain to a level generally of about 1200 ft., and the tilting of its surface to give a general summit level falling from south-east to north-west. The Central Plateau between Portomouro and Lugo, between La Coruña and Orense, remains an area of subdued relief, with rolling hills and sluggish streams of dendritic drainage. The only exceptional features are those

119

associated with recent vulcanicity such as Pico Sagro, south-east of Santiago.

On the western edge lies the considerable north–south rift of Portomouro-Tuy, floored with recent alluvium and drained by small subsequent streams. Into this depression the upland rivers descend abruptly from their local plateau base levels and along its eastern flank they have incised deep, narrow and precipitous valleys.

On the Atlantic side of this depression lie the somewhat smaller residual blocks isolated by the intensity of grid faulting. The Finisterre block is of considerable size, and the fault-zone separating it from the Central Plateau is represented only by faint and irregular depressions. Between these outlying pre-Cambrian blocks lies the district of the long and deep Rias Bajas, produced by faulting and later submerged, often with island strings at their mouths.

To the north of the Finisterre–Central Plateau blocks lies the less regularly faulted littoral area of the Rias Altas. Here later submergence has produced a series of large forked and arc-shaped cliffed inlets such as that between La Coruña and El Ferrol. In these inlets, shallower generally than the Rias Bajas, there are often large sandbanks. Here the plateau edge lies almost immediately behind the coast leaving only narrow stretches of lowland between it and the sea.

South of the Miño fault-valley lies the most elevated part of the granitic block. Uptilting in this south-east corner (Orense) has produced the Sierras de San Mamed and de Queija, which rise to almost 5000 ft. above sea-level. This considerable elevation of an old mature surface of low relief, has produced river rejuvenation, so that vertical river erosion is now active over the whole area. A few residual peaks alone remain of the old plateau surface. If therefore the central area may be regarded as a besieged old plateau, Orense province represents an old block conquered and riven by later forces. The Portuguese frontier which lies well to the south of the main latitudinal watershed is approximately the line of reappearance of a relatively undisturbed granitic plateau.

The eastern limit of the Galician region is demarcated by

the high glaciated mountains of the Western Cantabrian Cordilleras and the more recent faulted and folded Montañas de León and the Sierra Cabrera. In each case relative structural and topographic simplicity is replaced by complexity and irregularity.

Climate. Over this old Galician block the climatic elements are dominantly maritime. The Atlantic cyclone streams bring evenly distributed rainfall to all areas. Heaviest on the west facing residual blocks (generally over 80 ins.), lightest on the interior plateau (between 28 and 40 ins.), precipitation has but a faintly marked winter maximum. Fluctuating totals from year to year (mainly in the summer months) are, however, considerable. At Pontevedra, where the rainfall régime is regarded as relatively stable, the variations in combined July and August readings may be illustrated thus:

1912	. .	10·9 ins.
1921	. .	1·4 ,,
1931	. .	8·5 ,,
1937	. .	1·1 ,,

Even so the contrast between summer weather in Old Castile and Galicia can be quite startling. A sudden transition from a sunny brassy sky at León to a soaking Scotch mist at Orense is common enough. Orense itself, which in the long dry periods seems sufficiently Mediterranean in character, has umbrella-making as one of its chief activities. Open balconies characteristic of dry Spain are here glazed, so that La Coruña, one of the towns most exposed to Atlantic gales, has become famous for its glittering *miradores* and is known as the 'crystal city'.

This relatively even distribution of rainfall and cloudiness is associated with fair uniformity of temperature. Temperatures rarely fall anywhere below freezing point, and in most areas a January mean minimum of 50° F. is normal. Ranges are greatest on the interior plateau where winter snowfalls are paralleled by hot, fairly dry summers. The smallest temperature ranges and the highest mean minima are recorded in the Rias Bajas area. July means are in all areas about 70° F. or slightly lower.

Degree of exposure to the prevailing maritime westerly winds is of considerable importance. Those coastal hills which have the heaviest and most constant orographically concentrated cyclonic rains, are also the most windswept. Thus, although altitude is relatively low and dry-bulb thermometer readings generally high, the climate is bleak. Between the sheltered valleys of the west coast stand the residual wet and windswept ancient blocks that not only are in themselves climatically rather repellent, but also serve to isolate each lower valley floor. In the region of the Rias Altas sheltered coastal pockets are few and small, and the lack of any hinterland depression makes them extremely isolated climatically and topographically. Behind the hills the sheltered Tuy-Portomouro depression, with lower rainfall and more insolation, stands out in attractive contrast and serves to link the lower valleys.

Farther to the east the Lugo plateau presents a picture of general winter bleakness. This is broken only by the valley of the upper Miño. Orense province, by virtue of its greater dissection and despite its greater average elevation, has more sheltered land and therefore on average a more attractive climate.

Climatically, as topographically, the eastern mountain borders of Asturias and León are wild regions of highland climates, where the extreme conditions of the continental interior extend north-westwards up the valley gorges.

Galicia has no important mineral resources. Traces of gold and tin near Padrón merely confirm other evidence of early small-scale extraction. Near Vivero small low-grade iron deposits are worked, but are much less important than those of Asturias and Navarre. Their coastal location both explains their exploitation and ensures that they have but little effect on the life of Galicia as a whole.

The only two large towns of the region, Vigo and La Coruña, and the naval arsenal of El Ferrol belong not to

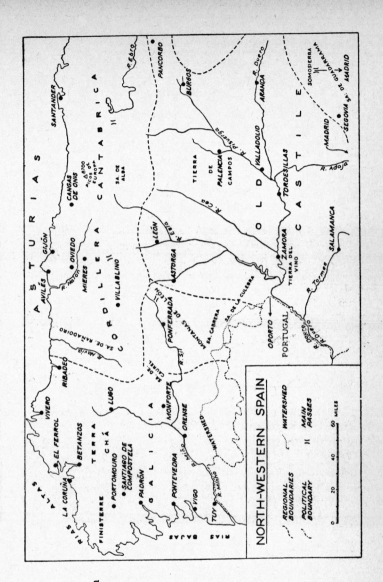

NORTH-WESTERN SPAIN

REGIONAL BOUNDARIES ⌒⌒ WATERSHED
POLITICAL BOUNDARY ⌁⌁ MAIN PASSES ‖

0   20   40   60 MILES

Galicia but to Spain. As noted in Chapter VII these ports are the Spanish equivalents of Brest and Cherbourg and through them Spain makes most of its Atlantic contacts.

The Gallegos are dependent in the main upon the agricultural resources of their region, and the distribution of population is a clear indication of relative potentialities. Population density is high, considering the small amount of urban development, averaging 130 per square mile on the bleak central plateau of the 'Terra Chá', and rising to over 700 in the lowlands of the Rias Bajas, Orense and Betanzos. Great stretches of the Finisterre plateau, of the 'Terra Chá' and the eastern and south-eastern hills are practically uninhabited, while the intensity of settlement of the more favoured land is only equalled in Spain by that of the Valencian 'huertas'.

This high density of an almost entirely agrarian population is made possible only by relative climatic benevolence. Soils vary considerably in small areas, particularly in the peripheral sub-regions of broken terrain. Predominantly, however, they are all derived from igneous rocks, and have a coarse sandy texture and a low lime content. Strongly leached by the heavy rainfall during most of each year, they are chemically and structurally somewhat poor soils. Moreover the rapidity of water percolation through these light sands reduces effective precipitation to some one-third of the total, and available groundwater is frequently as low as 10% of the rainfall. The only regions exceptional to this pattern are (a) those of poor drainage and marsh formation east of Lugo, and (b) the richer mixed soils in the Tuy-Padrón depression. In Galicia, therefore, we encounter a unique pattern of small-scale irrigation—necessary even where the rainfall rises over 50 inches per annum. This irrigation is designed to disperse plentiful water as constantly as is possible over thin and hungry soils.

The range of crops that can be grown in Galicia is considerable, but their regional importance closely reflects the controls exercised by relief and climate.

On the Central Plateau and in Finisterre important crops in order of areal importance are rye and potatoes, with wheat a poor third. In the Rias Bajas, maize is more important than all other crops put together, with vines and mixed tree-crops having some emphasis. Pontevedra province alone produces nearly 40% of the Spanish maize crop. Rye, wheat and potatoes are less important here than in any other part of Galicia.

To the south-east, in Orense, under conditions less bleak and less maritime, maize and vines dominate the sheltered valleys, while rye and potatoes are the crops of the highlands. In the humid blustery north-east maize, wheat and the vine are cultivated in the more sheltered basins—particularly around Betanzos, with rye and potatoes dominant elsewhere.

Generally maize and vines are confined to the sheltered Rias Bajas lands below about 800 ft. altitude. Rye predominates at heights over about 1200 ft. with wheat and potatoes in the intermediate zone. Tree-crops are only important in the lowlands.

Yields even in the least favoured regions are surprisingly high, considering soil poverty. Maize yields on irrigated lands of the south-west are comparable with those of Iowa, and the yields of wheat in Lugo are higher than those of Cardiganshire, a not dissimilar region.

The livestock population is of considerable size, the density both of cattle and pigs being the highest for any region in Spain. This largely results from the continuous supply of forage, and also reflects the dual value of maize as bread grain and as fodder.

These high yields and densities of crops and livestock, and the mixed nature of agriculture are both cause and effect of the nature and density of the human population.

The Gallegos are fishermen and peasants. They are a by-word in Spain for thriftiness and energy; and also, unjustifiably, the term Gallego has come to mean a boor, a country bumpkin. (In parenthesis it may be remarked that the inhabitants of Lugo have a similar reputation within Galicia itself!) They are, it is true, comparatively conservative and often very parochial; 16th century Camões in the Lusiads wrote of 'Cautious Galicia'.

The attributes of the Gallego are essentially those of his land. The suave climate of the south-west in which the Aleppo or Maritime Pine and the exotic eucalypts double their normal rate of growth is not alone sufficient to supply the rude plenty of cider, local wine, maize and rye bread, meat, milk and fruit. The thin leached soils need frequent and careful cultivation and nourishment. Irrigation (which is used on some 150,000 acres) is necessary for the full utilisation of the abundant water. The hill-slopes need terracing, the watercourses controlling. All this has been done by peasants living mainly under a subsistence economy, but unlike the cultivators of the Meseta, left undisturbed to build their landscape over a thousand years.

Virtually all the resources available have been utilised. Most houses are constructed of great granite slabs. Granite posts also support the vines—one might say that every cultivator has his own granite quarry in his garden. On the schists, vertical sheets of slate form the walls, and cover the rooftops and chimneys. The pines are stripped of their lower branches for fuel until they look like palm-trees with their lonely top clumps of foliage. Furze is encouraged to grow on fallow land to supply fodder, cattle bedding and fuel. The coarse rock fragments left after quarrying are used for semi-hydroponic cultivation (i.e. growing plants in heavily charged liquids).

In this way the carrying capacity of the land has been built up, and the population has grown. The population growth has however now outstripped the land's capacity for development. Properties have become rapidly smaller and while landholdings have traditionally been minute, during the last eighty years fragmentation of holdings has grown apace. Seasonal migration for harvest work as far afield as Andalusia, and permanent emigration outside the region have become normal.

In Galicia itself there seems little prospect for the large-scale development of alternative sources of employment. Water-power resources alone are insufficient. An increase in agricultural wealth seems almost as remote a possibility. Galician society has grown up in dispersed hamlets and on the plateau lands in lonely dispersed farmhouses. The *horreo*, the stone granary possessed by each household—so typical of

Galicia and the Asturias—also typifies the parochial isolation of each member of the community. The acquired self-sufficiency makes for isolation, mental and material, and the Gallego has now tended to become closed in behind his traditional modes of life. So, too, of Galicia as a whole; since the Reconquista started Galicia has become more and more remote from the mainstreams of Spanish life. During the conquest of León, the main surge came from the Asturias rather than from Galicia proper. The territory stretching between León and Zamora has never appeared very attractive to Gallegan eyes.

Communications have done little to break down this isolation. The main railways connect Madrid with the Atlantic ports rather than serve Galicia. Internal communications except between the provincial capitals are not good, and Galician immobility is still typified by the 'Carro Chirion' (the screeching cart) pulled by large slow oxen.

THE ASTURIAS

Asturias comprises the main Cantabrian Cordilleras and the Biscayan littoral. The dominating geographical factors are structure and relief.

The region is composed of a variety of rocks ranging from early Palaeozoic to Recent in age. In general, the older and more resistant rocks are dominant in the high Asturias west of Santander, the more recent Secondary series in the east. In detail, however, there is extreme structural complexity—mainly due to Hercynian and Tertiary tectonic action.

The basic pre-Carboniferous structures were considerably elevated, faulted and folded during the Hercynian orogenesis. The main east–west trend lines, including that of the coastline, were defined at this period. Against the old Galician platform the trend lines splayed north and south in complex arcuate form. Later deposition was probably discontinuous; and further erosion resulted in the survival of the Carboniferous series only in small structural and topographical basins such as that of the Oviedo coalfield. Farther to the east, Mesozoic beds covered extensive areas. These are mainly represented by Jurassic and Cretaceous series in the Santander area, and by considerable Cretaceous masking of underlying rocks in Navarre.

At the close of the Cretaceous period, the Alpine orogeny introduced a new series of disturbances, and by late Tertiary times the whole region of the Cantabrians and the Pyrenees has been upthrust, folded and faulted.

The area of greatest disturbance of old structures lay between the western granite block and the Picos de Europa. Elevation was considerable, and the structural trends increased in complexity. Secondary east–west trend lines appeared; and where these met the old Hercynian alignments the interaction of tectonic forces was most intense—as at the Picos de Europa. North–south structural trends on the Galician rim were strengthened, and subsidiary longitudinal alignments appeared on the northern flanks of the main Cordilleras. On the southern flanks movement was more subdued, and the Cantabrian structures pass in fairly simple fashion under the later deposits of the Douro basin.

In this western zone, Secondary and Tertiary beds have survived erosion in isolated outliers as at Monforte, the upper valleys of the Sil and Esla, and in the Jurassic iron ore beds.

East of the Picos de Europa and extending into Navarre, the geological landscape is dominated by folded Secondary and Tertiary rocks through which the primary substratum occasionally emerges in belts of low hills that show the old east–west alignment.

There is no well-marked structural change that defines the eastern limit of the Asturian region; but between Santander and Bilbao there lies a transition zone in which tectonic disturbance becomes rapidly of less significance and Palaeozoic rocks outcrop less and less frequently towards the east.

Topographically the Asturian region has its core or heartland in the area enclosed by the 3000-ft. contour, and it further includes the Biscayan littoral. On the east, the boundary between Asturias and Navarre is marked by a transition from mountains to hills. To the west the boundary is more abruptly and clearly marked by a fall from high sierras to the subdued relief of the Galician plateau.

The character of relief corresponds closely to the structural pattern. The central east–west ranges rise to over 6000 ft., and form a continuous and fairly simple watershed from the source of the Sil in the west to the Esla in the east. Northward from this central Cordillera, mountain blocks of considerable ruggedness extend almost to the coastline of the Bay of Biscay. There is no continuous coastal plain but rather dispersed lowlands only faintly connected by ill-defined lateral depressions. On this generally concordant coast there are few inlets of any size. On the southern (Douro) side of the watershed there is by contrast a more even general slope from crest to lowland.

On the Galician border the simple alignment disappears, and is replaced by splayed mountain ranges between which lie the basins of the Navia and upper Sil. This isolation of upland depressions between high sierras attains its greatest extent around Ponferrada which properly lies in the threshold region between Galicia and León.

East of the Esla headwaters lie the most Alpine of the mountain ranges, the Sierra de Alba and the Picos de Europa, which rise to over 9000 ft. Here glaciation and dissection of mainly limestone rocks have only increased the complexity of an old structural knot zone where Hercynian and Alpine trend lines join in an immense structural upheaval. From far out in the Bay of Biscay these serrated towering peaks form an impressive landmark.

Still farther eastwards the Cordillera decreases in altitude and becomes less wide, until in the zone between Santander and the upper Ebro, it degenerates into a series of dissected mountain blocks rising to between 5000 and 6000 ft. in height. Structural trends remain of some importance, but differential erosion of the various Secondary and Tertiary beds is of greater topographical significance. This is also the zone in which the Iberian mountains approach to the southern flanks of the Cantabrians. The divides between the Biscayan rivers, the Douro system, and the upper Ebro are ill-defined and the whole watershed zone is difficult to group with any specific region; there is, however, at the same time little human justification for its separation as a corridor zone.

The boundary between Asturias and Navarre is topographically defined by a marked eastward transition from mountains to hills. Behind Bilbao a multitude of small streams pierce the Tertiary folds and rarely are the interfluves of altitude greater than 3000 ft.

The climate and weather of the Asturias accentuate its mountain character and heighten the contrast between this rugged region and the Douro basin to the south.

Climate. Along the whole north-facing stretch of the Asturian Cordillera and the coastal area maritime cyclonic conditions predominate, bringing heavy rainfall of over 50 ins. to a belt some 50 to 60 miles wide. Where the mountain ranges are most broken, and where their alignment runs north to south, this rainy zone belt is widest. Behind the Picos de Europa, however, a considerable 'rain shadow' effect prolongs the relative aridity of the interior Meseta northwards to within 20 miles of the coast. The northern rainy zone is thus hourglass shaped with a narrow central waist; in this latter zone high altitude, relatively low precipitation and the preponderance of limestone surfaces combine to make it the least attractive part of Atlantic Iberia.

On the southern flanks in general the maritime mountain conditions extend down to about the 3000-ft. contour. Within a zone between 5000 and 2700 ft. in altitude there is in fact a slow transition to Meseta conditions: mean summer temperatures rise while mean winter temperatures of the inhabited lands fall, and precipitation decreases in quantity and increases in seasonality.

In Asturias proper, seasonal variations in precipitation are generally small; and of greater local importance is the proportion of precipitation which falls as snow. While this latter is largely controlled by altitude, aspect and exposure appear as the decisive factors in determining rainfall quantities, and also air humidity.

Absolute mean temperatures range on the average between 50° and 68° F., and the mean diurnal average (rarely exceeding 7° F.) reveals the relative constancy of climatic conditions. However, even more than in Galicia, weather is finally governed by terrain. The tree-line lies at about 7000 ft., but the sheltered valleys and coastal plains alone have long thermal growing seasons. This is a land of extremes: at Santander flourishes the lemon tree—one of the most sensitive of subtropical tree-crops—while on the high Sierras bleak winds and storm-cloud skies alternate over poor heaths and bare screes.

The continuing theme throughout the whole human and ecological geography of the Asturias is one of local isolation.

In the sierras and coastal mountains cultivable land is restricted to small well-watered pockets of alluvium. In these small pockets the leached forest soils are derived from a greater variety of parent rocks than are those of Galicia, and therefore although more restricted in area, are more fertile.

The vine and the olive are almost completely debarred because of the coolness of the cloudy and humid winters, and citrus fruit only succeeds in a few especially favoured areas. The apple is the only important tree-crop, especially in the littoral region between Oviedo and Galician Vivero, and in this district cider replaces wine. For the rest, cultivation is concerned with a variety of temperate food crops. Diversification, made possible by climate, is also encouraged by the self-sufficient peasant farming of the lonely valleys.

Rural life, both now and for millennia, has been dominated by pastoralism. Mountain summer pastures and valley hay form the basis for the rearing of large numbers of general-purpose cattle more important for milk than for meat. The density of the livestock population is extraordinarily high, considering the low carrying capacity of the high mountain lands, and is only made possible by mountain transhumance.

The summer movement to upland pastures of milch cows, horses and sheep is extensively practised on full Alpine scale west of Santander. On the southern side of the main watershed this transhumant pastoralism has spread downward into the high tablelands of León and Castile, the original vertical migration becoming modified into a regional movement between the dry arable lands and the hill grassland. From this development stemmed the Mesta.

East of Santander transhumance is little practised, and in the Basquelands, as in the more favoured Asturian coastal lowlands, a more sedentary mixed farming takes its place.

Asturian rural life is still dominated by the immediate needs of the inhabitants and herds of the small mountain villages. Settlement is characterised by dispersed hamlets rather than by isolated farmsteads. Here, as in Galicia, local self-sufficiency predominates; minute fields and rugged stone houses each with its own *horreo*, cluster together in the narrow valleys, and are encircled by the open, wooded hills which until recently were largely owned and grazed in commonalty. Urban development has hitherto been too small to make much economic impact on the countryside.

Unlike Galicia, the Asturian region possesses a considerable number of mineral resources. The deposits are scattered in the small structural basins in which Carboniferous coal measures and Jurassic iron beds in particular have survived. Unfortunately for the region the remoteness, inaccessibility and small size of most of the Cantabrian mineral fields make them uneconomic of operation in face of competition from abroad. The only important centres of operation now lie around Oviedo and Santander.

Oviedo, which has a population of 135,000, lies in a relatively fertile agricultural depression between the Nalon river and the Cangas de Onís littoral to the north-east. In this area was born the first independent Spanish kingdom. To the west of the town lie considerable deposits of iron ore which because of their high silica content and low Fe content (averaging 30%) have been but little worked. To the south and east of Oviedo stretches a thousand square miles of the nation's most important coalfields, producing over 75% of the annual Spanish output of 15 million tons. Most of the workings lie in the steep, narrow valleys of the Nalon and its tributaries, in the sides of which drifts have been driven through the outcrops into the main seams of the hills. In these valleys a constellation of secondary towns such as Mieres and Lera have grown up around Oviedo to form an industrial region second only to that of Catalonia.

The Asturian region with its concordant cliffed coast has few good natural harbours. One of these, Gijón, lies north-east of the Nalon basin, and although by no means easy of access from Oviedo, has become the second largest Spanish port for weight of goods handled. This considerable growth results not only from the fact that the Oviedo region has to import all its raw materials and much of its food from outside. The iron and steel making and engineering of the Nalon basin has in fact developed on local fuel and imported ores, and is complementary to Santander and Bilbao where the situation is reversed. In recent years the harnessing of some of the considerable water power resources of this pluviose mountain region has further accelerated the century-old industrialisation.

Exploitation of the lean Jurassic iron ores is problematical. Avilés itself, for which a sizable future as a steel centre is planned, is only likely to grow, as have Oviedo and Gijón, on local fuels and imported ores. As the ore resources of Navarre and Santander become depleted, supplies may be drawn from Vivero. Local ores are technically usable but costs would probably make Avilés non-competitive on world markets.

The Santander industrial centre, less important than that of Oviedo, has a similar general location, although here development has taken place on the coastal plain. The satellite towns of Cabargo and Camargo are almost entirely iron mining settlements, and thus contrast with the more general industrial character of the Nalon towns. The hematite ores of reasonable quality have been, and still are, almost entirely shipped either to Gijón or to foreign markets.

Both of these industrial regions, unlike those of Navarre, have always been hampered by the extreme difficulty of communication with the rest of Spain. In both cases there are well-defined passes through the Cantabrian Cordillera to the Douro lands. Whilst these were perfectly suitable for the movement of pastoralist settlers and their flocks on to the Meseta, they present considerable difficulties to bulk transport by road or rail. Steep gradients and the great extent of negative land combine to raise engineering and maintenance costs to a high level. Not until the hydro-electric potential of the Cantabrians is further exploited and transmission lines extended into Castile can either the resources of the Asturias be easily tapped for the benefit of Spain as a whole, or the Asturian region itself be closely associated with national economic life.

The industrial north has developed in topographic and social isolation. Having been forced to look outward to the sea, it has been unable to extend the range of its activities even as much as has Catalonia, which possesses much poorer basic resources.

Therefore, although urban growth has tended to encourage the normal modern movement of population down from the high sierras, much of the life of the region is still bucolically isolated and self-centred. Even the few towns compare most unfavourably in sophistication with analogous centres in Mediterranean Spain and the neighbouring regions of Navarre and Galicia.

THE THRESHOLD OF LEÓN

As noted earlier, the transition from the Asturian mountains to the Douro basin is not abrupt. A few hundred yards from the source of the easternmost tributary of the Sil rises the Etuerto which flows south-eastwards past Astorga through rapidly opening tablelands to join the Esla and Douro. The Sil-Etuerto depression routeway, commanded by Astorga and Ponferrada, has for long been the main corridor for movement between Galicia and the Meseta. Its physical difficulties lie not in the watershed area but in the gorge tract of the middle Sil.

In the southern half of this region there is little difference between the terrain of the Palaeozoic ranges of the Sierra Cabrera and the elevated and dissected Orense granite region. To the south-east the hills are extended to within 20 miles of Zamora by the Sierra de la Culebra thus completing the isolation of the Esla basin from the Atlantic lands. Through the east–west aligned ranges runs a well-marked depression—westwards from the Tera valley to Ribadavia on the Miño. This has been less important historically than the northern corridor because although it has slighter gradients, it has a longer traverse of negative land. The routeway now carries an arterial road and will have the planned Zamora–Orense–Santiago railroad. Significantly there are no large settlements along this southern corridor.

The threshold nature of this region is more important than any individuality it may possess in its own right.

The physical transition from west to east has a climatic parallel although here the change is fairly abrupt along the eastern boundary. Orographic effects extend pluviose Atlantic conditions almost to Astorga and then give way to relative aridity. Summer dryness does not become extreme but the incidence of rainfall becomes less frequent and more violent. Diurnal ranges rise considerably. The effect of altitude on climate must also be remembered—Astorga lies at a height of 2850 ft., Monforte 1260 ft.

In general then the Esla basin as viewed by a Gallego from the Montanas de León raises little feeling of envy or desire. To the west lies the constant green of the Sil valley, to the east the seasonal brown and green rhythm of the treeless plains. Only to the peoples of the Sierras has this threshold region been a valued gateway into the interior. To the inhabitants of the well-watered and suave Rias Bajas, movement up the Sil means a loss rather than a gain in wealth.

OLD CASTILE

This is the region of the middle Douro basin. Its limits are coterminous with those of the northern Meseta Tertiary rocks, and it includes the old kingdoms of León and Castile. During the Reconquista this territory was peopled from the Galician hills and the Asturian mountains, who here found a transition zone in which their modes of life were modified rather than revolutionised. To the Asturian the move into Old

Castile was a descent from high sierras to relative lowland, to the Galician it was an ascent to a high tableland. The most important single fact about this northern part of the Meseta is its elevation—the whole area has an altitude greater than 1500 ft. and much of it lies over 2500 ft.

In this elevated basin, the surface geology is of more significance than the underlying rock structure. Exposed rocks are entirely Tertiary in age, but north of the Douro these are largely masked by recent outwash material brought down from the Cantabrian Cordillera. The Tertiary limestones, sandstones and clays were deposited by river and lake action over a depressed Palaeozoic and Archaean substratum, and largely retain their horizontality. On their north and north-west limits the Asturian and León Palaeozoic rocks come to the surface: to the south and south-west emerge the Archaean granites of north Portugal and the Central Sierras. The eastern boundary is that of the secondary rocks of the Iberian mountains into which stretches the great Tertiary embayment of Soria.

The Douro basin is thus not only almost encircled by high mountains but also isolated within a circle of separate and distinct geological landscapes.

All the important rivers of Old Castile rise outside the region. The Douro has its headwaters in the Iberian mountains, and its upper catchment basin in the elevated Tertiary basin of Soria. Between Soria and Imazán lies a Tertiary zone uplifted in the western rim of the Iberid folds, and along this relatively easily eroded line the upper Douro has cut a deep mountain valley westward. This hill-stream character is retained downstream as far as Aranda, at which point the Douro emerges on the undisturbed tableland. Across this old Tertiary erosion surface the Douro runs in an open mature valley west to Zamora. Immediately west of its confluence with the Esla, it plunges down from its local base-level thence to traverse the lower but more rugged and dissected granite lands of northern Portugal.

From the Central Sierras flow a small number of tributaries of which the Tormes and Adaja are the most important. Their relatively small volume and seasonally fluctuating flow have neither markedly worn down the old mesa-dotted peneplain nor caused much alluvial infill. South of the Douro the landscape is marked by senility.

From the north flow the larger and more numerous tributaries of Atlantic Highland régime. The three main drainage systems of the Esla, Cea and Pisuerga derive most of their water from the Cantabrian Cordillera. Here the snow-melt of summer and the heavy (only slightly seasonal) rainfall are drained south in a close network of large and swift rivers. These have not only considerably eroded the old Tertiary surface, but also masked it to a large extent with detritus which grades from coarse gravels in the piedmont zone to fine silts near the Douro. The resulting landscape is a little more undulating and less geometrically stark than that farther south, and the residuals, though still impressive, are not quite so prominent.

The unbalance between the strength of the Douro's left and right bank tributaries is also emphasised by the asymmetry of the main drainage lines, the main axis of the Douro itself lying well to the south of the valley centre. This offsetting is primarily the result of asymmetry in the underlying geological structure. Traverses north and south from the Douro itself illustrate the resulting zonation. Northwards the open main valley gives way to a partly silt-covered Tertiary surface which rises gradually to some 2000 ft. North of a line connecting Palencia and Benavente, the silts and Tertiary measures become increasingly replaced by coarse gravels—the exception being the Campos claylands of Palencia and the limestone Paramos near León. This upper sloping terrace rises to a height of between 2500 and 2800 ft., at which levels it gives way to a hilly upland rim which in turn is overlooked by the high Sierras of Asturias.

A traverse southward from the Douro passes through the same corresponding zones, but here the Tertiary surface is of greater relative extent and the outwash zone no longer lies in great terraces but is represented by usually discontinuous

detritus cones. Immediately behind these is a compressed upland rim that passes without abruptness into the relatively
subdued relief of the granitic Central Sierras.

In each of these sub-regions, topographical monotony is
broken only by the minor effects of differential weathering and
erosion. North of Valladolid the residual survival of Tertiary
limestones forms the Montes de Torozas, while around the
lower Cea similar limestones have produced barren waterless
plains.

The climate of Old Castile has continentality as its main
characteristic, this partly the result of, and accentuated by, the
elevation of the basin as a whole. By no means as extreme in
character as that of the southern Meseta or the Iberian mountains, the regional climate is hotter in summer, colder in
winter and always drier than the upland regions hitherto
examined.

The typical thermal range lies between mean January
temperatures just above freezing point to means of over 70° F.
in July and August. The diurnal minima and maxima concealed within these means express more accurately the nature
of the climate—20° F. and 50° F. at midwinter and 45° F.
and 100° F. in summer. Mean temperatures at León and
Burgos are some 4°–5° F. lower than those at Valladolid and
Salamanca, a natural result of their altitude and exposure to
mountain winds.

Precipitation in the region as a whole is between 15 ins.
and 25 ins. per annum, and regional differences appear not
only in the rainfall totals but also in the régimes, depending on
the type of interaction between Atlantic and interior air masses.

During winter high pressure developed over the Meseta as a
whole often prevents the incursion of the maritime air masses.
This pressure barrier is least effective along the upland rim
on which lie Burgos and León. There, rain-bearing winds
breaking through the northern passes ensure that no month
receives less than 0·8 in. out of an annual average of over
20 ins. A marked May maximum results from the early
breakdown of winter pressure conditions. In the lower lands
of the Douro, the winter outflowing cold air is but slowly

replaced by local convectional effects. Generally mild pressure stability becomes stronger throughout the summer until the retreat of the Azores high and local heating bring an autumn maximum. Salamanca with an annual total of 11 ins. experiences a dry July and August and a slight September maximum.

The climatic zonation in general duplicates that of topography but the ecological effect of the climate as a whole is inhibitive. Old Castile lies intermediate between the lands of the Atlantic on one hand and of New Castile, the Ebro and the south on the other. Neither temperate nor sub-tropical tree-crops are of much importance, commercial viticulture is confined to the extreme west, while of the sown field-crops only the winter-hardy or drought-escaping types succeed. In spite of this apparent poverty of environment, it must be remembered that while optimum climatic conditions exist for no crop-plants, marginal cultivation of many crops, from humid and dry lands, highland and lowland, north and south, is possible. In Old Castile there exist many more opportunities for diversification than are to be found in the rest of the Meseta.

The soils of the region are varied but except for one group they are more fertile than the podsols of the pluviose lands. The restricted amount of leaching of soluble salts, and the long periods of high temperature have produced in particular fairly stable nitrogenous conditions.

The exceptional soil groups are those derived from Archaean rocks and non-calcareous sandstones. In Galicia the sandy granitic soils of low inherent fertility are rendered usable by the abundance of water. In Old Castile the sandy soils with low lime content have no such compensations. The western corner of the region near Zamora has become the 'Tierra del Vino' of Old Castile, because climatic conditions permit the large-scale growing of the vine on granite soils unsuitable for more demanding crops. On the other hand, where these granitic soils are more heavily leached, and where temperature conditions are least favourable, then their real poverty is revealed. South and west of Salamanca and along the edge of the Central Sierras lie the poorest areas of Old Castile.

Where the Tertiary rocks are exposed, chemical fertility of the soil is of a higher order and the degree of admixture of calcareous and non-calcareous material becomes of first importance. South of the Douro calcareous content is low, and this, together with an acute shortage of water and the heat of summer, severely restrict agriculture. Dry-farming of cereals and fallow grazing of transhumant sheep alone are possible.

North of the Douro the soils are more productive. Where limestone alone is present the formation of soil is slow and sporadic, but where the calcareous elements are combined with silts and clays conditions are good. Thus on the intermediate slopes lying in an east–west belt just north of Palencia are the best agricultural lands. Climatic controls still encourage the predominance of cereals, but yields are relatively high. The Tierra del Campos north-west of Palencia is the 'Tierra del Pan' (land of bread) of Old Castile.

On the higher slopes and in much of the Esla basin the coarse gravels derived from the ring of Palaeozoic rocks have been little mixed with the underlying Tertiaries and give light, porous and chemically poor soils in a zone of relatively harsh climate.

On the lowest northern slopes, the soils are similar in type to those south of the Douro, but with higher calcareous content. Sporadic formation of Terra Rossa occurs where special conditions of climate and parent-rock exist. Fertility is high and structure good, but only where irrigation water is available can the Terra Rossa be intensively worked.

Lastly there are the alluviums of the Douro and its right-bank tributaries. In these valleys soil characteristics are less important—the principal feature is the availability or otherwise of irrigation water.

Considerable emphasis has been placed on the physical characteristics of Old Castile for two main reasons. First, the Douro basin has no mineral wealth of any significance, and all human life now depends either on the use of agricultural resources or on the positional importance attached to a few settlement sites. The development of irrigation is only possible

in a few restricted areas, and so here we see the direct action
of a limited number of geographical factors. Secondly, the
Spanish way of life and much of that of Spanish America was
born in these lands of Old Castile. The environment, by no
means attractive in any absolute sense, could be made use of
by the peoples of the high Asturias: here they developed an
ability to cope with bitter cold winters, harsh hot summers,
climatic variability and a great variety of terrain—an ability
that alone can explain the fortitude and adaptability of the
Conquistadores of the New World.

A consideration of the settlement pattern serves to emphasise
the lack of uniformity within the region and to illustrate the
main characteristics of its human geography.

Encircling the main Tertiary basin (except on the west) lies
an outer belt of large cities and towns, all, with but two exceptions, lying at altitudes of between 2500 and 2800 ft.—
Salamanca, Ávila, Segovia, Aranda, Burgos, Herrera, León,
La Beñeza. All these settlements lie on the upland rim, the
zone where the mountain valleys of the incoming rivers become more mature and open. Their actual sites are not where
the mountain rivers debouch, but where the high marginal
rim drops down to the lower basin—they are not pass towns
but the centres of threshold regions. The distinction is that
between Pancorbo which truly commands the Pisuerga–Ebro
pass, and Burgos which is a base from which the whole corridor
may be controlled from the west. Ávila and Segovia are
apparent exceptions because of their higher situations—over
3000 ft. Their function as regional centres and their positions
in the actual landscape reveal clearly enough their kinship to
other towns in this group.

Away from these regional and routeway centres, settlement
is sparsely nucleated in small farming villages and not dissimilar to the hamlets of the northern mountains. Around
León where soil and climate are at their local best, population
density is higher and settlement more scattered.

In the lowest lands of the Douro basin lie a series of riverside towns and cities stretching from Zamora to Valladolid.

Each of the larger settlements combines the functions of a regional market centre with that of a general route focus. Zamora is the centre for the Tierra del Vino and the gateway into the western granite-lands. From the north come the Esla and Cea routes, from the south the route from Ávila and Salamanca along the edge of the Tertiary basin. Valladolid, the largest city of Old Castile, with a population of 133,000, is the market centre for the Tierra del Pan and by reason of its nodal position once disputed the pre-eminence of Burgos and Madrid. On Valladolid converge the routes from Palencia and Burgos, from Soria and Aranda, and from Segovia and Ávila. North-westward the main communications cross transversely the drainage pattern to connect directly with Astorga and León, and through Tordesillas run the routes to Zamora and Salamanca.

Between these two settlement zones, upland rim and valley floor, lies a third and less distinct belt. From the upland rim and from the Douro valley, the kingdoms of Old Castile and León were conquered and controlled; but it was the intermediate lands that were settled and worked. This middle or Mesa belt is distinguished by the virtual absence of large towns. Palencia, the one exception, is only relatively large (with a population of some 51,000) and here since Roman times the fertility of the surrounding corn-lands has maintained true urban life. Once a royal residence and the site of the first Spanish university (1208), Palencia is now a quiet market town. For the rest the landscape is frugal and bare, small villages, inhabited almost entirely by farmers, merging into the landscape. Sometimes these hamlets as it were hide under the residual tabular hills, deriving shelter and even water from the stark limestone and clay mesas. Often they lie clustered around their large fortresslike churches, on some small stream or fertile pocket in the vast treeless plains. Everywhere there is still a sense of frontier life, of scorched earth.

THE NORTH-EAST

THE regions considered under this head are all associated
with the old kingdoms of Navarre and Aragon. Frankish
and Mediterranean influence is strong everywhere, except on
the bleak Iberian mountains which separated the territory
of Aragón from that of Castile.

NAVARRE

Navarre is a hill region lying between the high mountains of
the Asturias and the Pyrenees, between the upper Ebro basin
and the Bay of Biscay.

Structurally, Navarre is similar in character to the eastern
part of the Asturian region. Palaeozoic sedimentary and
crystalline rocks uplifted in Hercynian times were later overlain
by Mesozoic beds. Tertiary tectonic action then further
elevated and faulted the old core with its superincumbent
secondary rocks, although disturbance was slight compared
with that in the Pyrenees and Cantabrians. Mesozoic rocks
now form most of the exposed surface, pierced by Palaeozoic
inliers in the hills of the western Pyrenees, and overlain with
the Tertiary deposits of the Ebro basin on the southern edge
of the region.

The main structural effect on topography is to be observed
in the general east–west alignment of the four main hill ranges
in Vascongadas. This alignment is not everywhere pronounced
—for instance to the west of Bilbao the Las Encartaciones are
a confused jumble of hills. South of the main watershed, this
alignment is replaced by the major erosional terraces of the
Tertiary foothills. Differential erosion by the streams of the
dense hydrological network is more important in determining

the details of terrain. The drainage patterns trending north into the Bay of Biscay and south into the Ebro basin are super-imposed on the structural east–west trends; and the resultant incomplete grid dissection makes the depression routeways extremely tortuous. Although the passes are never high, gradients are often very steep.

The east–west watershed divides the region into two distinct zones. To the north lies Vascongadas, the true land of the Basques, forested rainy hill-land, much industrialised, and a part of Atlantic Spain. To the south lies Navarre proper, of drier mountain and valley flats, still mainly pastoral, and belonging much more to the Pyrenees and the interior. Always present, this distinction has become progressively more sharply marked. For example, the 1936 Right Wing Revolu-tion was a popular rising in southern Navarre, and the Requetés of the pastoral lands were soon in fierce conflict with the radical thinking industrial workers of Basque Bilbao.

Climatically, the whole region falls within the humid zone of Spain. San Sebastian has an annual average rainfall of over 52 ins., Bilbao 48 ins. Precipitation is fairly evenly distributed throughout the year, no month receiving much less than 3 ins. and slight maxima occurring in autumn and spring. Inland, away from the coastal hills, total precipitation decreases to some 30 ins. per annum, this drop being most marked towards the Ebro and least marked eastward towards the Pyrenees.

On the coast, mean monthly temperatures range between 50° F. and 70° F., associated with small diurnal ranges. Inland, conditions become more continental to the south, marked by lower minima and higher maxima; while in the Pyrenean zone altitudinal effects result in generally lower temperatures at all seasons.

In no part of Navarre is there any marked dead season due to aridity or adverse thermal conditions; and only in the high-est lands is there severe restriction on plant growth. The clima-tic differences between the northern and southern zones are exemplified by the greater emphasis in the Biscayan sub-region on diversified cultivation and dairy farming, while southern Navarre relies to a greater extent on cereals and general pur-

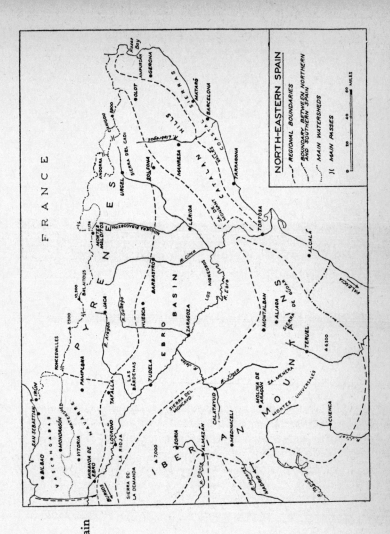

15 North-
Eastern Spain

pose cattle. It must be noted, however, that this difference is only one of degree, and in part results from the importance in the north of large urban markets for foodstuffs.

Basque speech, which once predominated in the whole of this region and which also was used in eastern Asturias and French Gascony, has now rather shrunken limits. Pamplona, Estella and Vitoria, once Basque centres, have become regional nucleii and route centres of Spain.

Pamplona itself and its hinterland are typical of southern Navarre. Now with a population of 105,000, the city is situated on a defensible hill-site within the basin of the river Arga, tributary to the Ebro. This basin (lying at 1300 ft. above sea-level) is surrounded on all sides by hills rising to about 3000 ft., once almost entirely forested but now considerably cleared. Communication with the surrounding areas is relatively easy, using the tortuous valleys of the Basque sierras, the Pyrenean foothills and the Sierra del Perdón to the south-west. Nevertheless the site of Pamplona, while excellent for a fortress centre in days of local self-sufficiency and for a market town in present days, is rather isolated.

Around Pamplona lie dispersed hamlets, each with a population of 200–300, almost entirely rural in function. These hamlets, rarely more than a mile apart, lie in the middle of their cultivated lands devoted mainly to wheat growing. Population pressure is relatively high, and fragmentation considerable. These piedmont settlements usually have strong links with the uplands of the Pyrenees, and transhumance of village flocks and herds is still practised to some extent. Towards the Ebro, villages became fewer and larger, and more like the Meseta settlements in character.

North of the watershed, the landscape is composed of smaller units. Intense dissection has produced a highly accidented topography, and the intermingling of cultivated lowland and forested hills is very intricate. Rural settlement is here mainly in the form of dispersed farmsteads each with its own main holding given over to temperate tree-crops (citrus on the coast), and to a variety of food and fodder plants. Every few miles lies a small local market town such as Guernica, the ancient seat of the Basque councils. The scene is extraordinarily reminiscent of Central Europe and, as J. Dantín Cereceda has pointed out, this region is Central European rather than Mediterranean in diet, clothing and general mode of life.

Vascongadas has been considerably affected by industrial and urban growth. San Sebastian in origin is a frontier fortress which owes its development as a holiday resort to the late 19th-century patronage of the Spanish Court fleeing from the summer heat of Madrid to a more pleasant clime. Irún, by contrast, is a simple frontier post and Spanish rail terminus.

Bilbao, originally a fishing village on the Nervión river, has grown during the last century into a thriving port and industrial centre (see Chapter VII). Its prosperity is derived from the Cretaceous iron ores lying to the west of the city. These ores, with an iron content of over 50%, and low phosphorus content, were of greatest value before the techniques of using high-phosphorus ore were fully adopted in Britain, France and Belgium. Some 220 million tons of ore have been mined up to now, almost all being exported. At Bilbao the chief Spanish iron and steel centre has developed, based on local ore and on coal imported from Oviedo and overseas. Of the city's 318,000 population, by far the biggest proportion is dependent either on ore extraction, or metallurgical processing and manufacture, or on the handling of the considerable export tonnage of iron and the import of fuel and other supplies. To the west lie mining villages, farther east scattered and small iron-making centres such as Mondragón and Beasain.

The impact of this recent industrialisation on the countryside has been considerable. The growth of urban markets for agricultural products has already stimulated intensive farming, and the development of a close network of road and rail communications has broken down rural isolation. Vascongadas, in spite of its agricultural productivity, has now become heavily dependent on imported supplies.

Future prosperity is by no means as assured. The best ores have been worked out, and total reserves are now only some 20 million tons. Apart from its iron ore the Bilbao area has few material advantages for manufacture, and Basque separatism has hardly endeared the region to the Central Government. As in the case of Oviedo, remoteness from the rest of Spain, although much less based on topographic inaccessibility, has made this zone of pluviose Spain a region apart. The relative contrast between urban and enterprising Vascongadas, and patriarchal pastoral southern Navarre serves to emphasise the separate character of the true Basques.

THE PYRENEES

The Pyrenean mountains extend for some 240 miles between Atlantic Biscay and the Mediterranean, lying well south of the narrowest neck of the isthmus. Structurally and topographically they are of considerable complexity, particularly so on the Spanish side of the main watershed. This mountain mass both unites and divides the people of the adjoining territory: unites in that mountain cultures straddle the political frontier, divides in that the main watershed from which the frontier only infrequently diverges does in fact separate different atmospheres and landscapes. A traveller crossing the Pyrenees is rarely left in doubt whether he is in France or Spain, hence the rather questionable dictum that Africa begins at the Pyrenees.

The present mountains owe their elevation to Tertiary tectonic action. Whether they should be regarded as true Alpine nappes or whether they are more akin to the Jura and other Foreland regions cannot here be discussed. Of greater importance is the fact that in the Pyrenees Tertiary movements uplifted, folded and faulted a whole series of beds ranging from Archaean crystalline rocks to Tertiary sedimentaries. The differing reactions to movement of these varying elements have produced distinct structural and topographical effects.

The oldest crystalline granites, schists and gneisses have been thrust upward and exposed by later erosion in great isolated and irregularly aligned blocks. Thus were formed the highest mountain masses of the Pyrenees—Balaitous, Montes Malditos, Canigou—which are weathered and glaciated into

smooth rather than savage forms. Around these blocks lie
faulted and metamorphosed Palaeozoic sedimentaries. These
resistant rocks, earlier disturbed by Hercynian orogenesis,
extend the full length of the Pyrenees. On them the forces of
glacial and water erosion have formed the most rugged and
dissected relief to be found in the region—as around the Pic
du Midi d'Ossau. The inner mountain zone, lying at altitudes
between 7000 and 10,000 ft., is made up of these old crystalline
rocks. Widest to the east of the Val d'Aragón, it has formed a
true if poor habitat for mountain cultures.

On the flanks of this mountain core lie more recent and
softer sedimentaries folded in east–west alignment. On the
French side this zone is comparatively narrow, and the north-
flowing streams are seldom diverted from their consequent
courses. The mountain basins such as that of Bedous are merely
erosional widenings of relatively straight valleys. On the
Spanish flank, however, a wide belt of Secondary and early
Tertiary rocks, intensively folded parallel to the main watershed, lies between the mountain core and the late Tertiary
Ebro basin. In this zone alternate hard and soft Triassic,
Cretaceous and even Eocene beds. The combined effect of
differential erosion and parallel folding has produced extreme
topographic and hydrographic complexity.

The valleys descending from the watershed run southward
for only short distances before they alternately break through
and run between high east–west ridges which succeed each
other like waves down to the plain of the Ebro. The southern
limit of the Pyrenean region lies where these ridges give way to
the high Tertiary terraces at Artesa, Barbastro, Huesca and
Tafalla. Glaciation has further confused the drainage pattern,
so that valleys and interfluves interlock in maze-like intricacy.
In such country the easiest routes are very far from being the
shortest. Huesca lies 45 miles from the watershed as the crow
flies but the road traverses 90 and the railway 120 miles of
poor highland to reach the summit passes.

In the relatively wide parallel valley basins, such as those
of Jaca and Seo de Urgél, have from time immemorial been
sited the settlements of the mountain people—fairly safe from

intrusion but equally remote from the world outside. The Pyrenees have always united these upland basin cultures, and rendered political frontiers ineffective as barriers. Pastoralists, refugees, smugglers have always found this true. The character of the Pyrenees as a 'divide' has only become important in recent times and then not so much because of the difficulty of crossing the mountains but a result of their increasing emptiness as compared with lands north and south.

A further division may be made on a topographic and human basis. West of the Aragón river the parallel ranges disappear and are replaced by the hills of Navarre, inhabited by the Basques. East of the Noguera Ribagorzina the lower Pyrenees merge with the Catalan hills, and complexity and altitude alike decrease. Here Romance speech and Mediterranean peoples and cultures have spread into the hills. Between these two extremity regions, the Pyrenees attain their greatest height, width and complexity and here the true highland cultures of Aragón and Sobrarbe have developed in their highest vernacular form.

There are few climatic statistics available for this region but those that exist, together with general ecological studies, give a sufficiently clear picture of the landscape. The Pyrenees have a mountain-modified climate, part rainy-Atlantic, part continental-Mediterranean.

Rainfall is heaviest in the west and on the high peaks. A narrow zone stretching from the Pic du Midi to the Atlantic receives over 100 ins. per annum. At a lower level but still over 3000 ft. annual precipitation ranges from 50 ins. in the west to 40 ins. in the east. Below the mountains proper rainfall decreases along with altitude and growing rain-shadow effects— e.g. Jaca has 29 ins.—until the aridity of the Ebro basin is reached. In the high mountain zone there is a slight winter rainfall maximum coinciding with general Atlantic conditions. At Jaca continental influences predominate, giving a June maximum and winter minimum. Snowfall is usually heavy in the sierras and most passes are closed for several weeks each year.

In the sierras mean monthly temperatures range from over 40° F. in summer to under 20° F. in winter; but differences in aspect and insolation produce considerable variations in thermal controls. In the lower lands temperatures rise rapidly, and the climate becomes a temperate version of the extreme Ebro conditions—Jaca 70° F. in June, 38° F. in January.

Soils vary enormously but in general there is observable a gradation from the thin, leached, lime-poor siallitic soils of the high mountains through the humid calcareous types found on the foothills to the dry calcareous soils of the Ebro trough. Only in the wider basins of the transverse sections of the high-land valleys is there any considerable alluvial deposition, and only in these terraced pockets is to be found much sedentary agriculture.

Most of the Pyrenees are still 'Pastos y Montes'—natural grass and forest. Woodland is scarcer on the southern flanks than on the north mainly because the tree-zone is so com-pressed between a low upper limit determined by winter harsh-ness and a high lower limit fixed by summer aridity. In the more rainy areas chestnut, beech and firs predominate but eastward these give way to pines and finally to scrub forest— *Monte Bajo*.

Resources are extremely limited. Agriculture is even more restricted than in the Asturias, because the habitable sheltered basins usually have deficient rainfall. Pastoralism of an Alpine transhumant character is dominant: cattle, sheep and swine pastured on the open mountainland are still often handled in commonalty, and partly fed on the mast of the woodlands.

In the small cultivable basins (such as that of Cerdagne on the Segre) are clustered the small stone-built hamlets. Some of these settlements have attained a more than local importance, e.g. Jaca and Seo de Urgel. Such centres of pre-Roman origin rose to eminence when the mountain tribes first began their descent into the Moslem-held foothills. Still small (Jaca has a population of a little over 5000, Urgel 3000), they have de-veloped into regional market and route centres. Added to the relative fertility of their tiny demesnes, the nodality resulting from the intersection of the latitudinal depressions by transverse valleys has produced some slight growth. Nowhere, however, is there any true urban development. Nor is there to be found much dispersed settlement, except the small dwellings and stables seasonally used for transhumance. Depopulation of the already sparsely inhabited highlands points rather to future decline rather than growth.

Of exploitable mineral wealth there is none, and the only Pyrenean treasure is the considerable water power potential and possibilities for water storage. The Segre river alone produces almost one-quarter of all Spanish hydro-electricity. Both the power and the water, however, are destined for use outside the region, the former in Barcelona, the latter in the 'huertas' of Lérida. The Pyrenees themselves remain unchanged in their lofty and often desolate isolation.

THE EBRO BASIN

Between the Pyrenees and the Iberian mountains lies a great triangular depression through which flows the Ebro. This basin is cut off from the sea by the Catalan hills and the eastern prolongation of the Iberian mountains, through which the Ebro cuts its way in a relatively narrow valley.

The Ebro basin is a great structural trough fundamentally similar to that of the northern Meseta. In this trough deposition has proceeded with little interruption at least since Cretaceous times. Post-Oligocene uplift resulted in the partial denudation of the early Tertiary erosion surface, and was followed by Miocene and Pliocene sedimentation. The Tertiary deposits are everywhere still relatively flat and undisturbed, and later erosion has produced a terraced or low tabular landscape of little variety.

Superimposed on the Tertiary beds north of the Ebro are the gravels and silts of the outwash apron below the Pyrenees. The great left-bank tributaries of the Ebro rising in the pluviose highlands bring down considerable volumes of silt and water into the trough, and have produced a landscape not dissimilar to that north of the Douro in Old Castile. The analogy is further strengthened by the lesser importance of the southern Ebro tributaries and the southward offsetting of the main drainage axis. There, however, comparison ends.

The Ebro basin has little topographic uniformity. A physiographic sub-division indicates the considerable compartmentalisation of the region, and helps to explain why historic Catalonia lapped over the Catalan hills to meet Aragón near the Cinca.

The Ebro rises in the Mesozoic Asturias and then, leaving its mountain valley, drops down into the Tertiary corridor which connects Old Castile and Aragón. The structural trough begins just below Miranda del Ebro and, continuing downstream to Tudela, forms the upper basin—La Rioja Alta. Around Logroño Miocene rocks form a narrow basin overlooked to the north by the hills of Navarre, and to the south by the high Sierra de la Demanda.

Near Tudela the depression opens out to form the main central basin which extends south-eastward to the confluence of the Cinca-Segre rivers. North from the Ebro there is a stepped landscape of open flats, extending for some 100 miles to Huesca and the Pyrenean foothills. South of the Ebro, the flats are narrower and soon give way to the high sierras of the Iberian mountains.

The third sub-region is the Cinca-Segre basin around Lérida. Here the lowland reached its greatest extent, but here also stream dissection and alluvial infill are dominant. The tabular hills of the central basin give way to lower interfluves of the dense wide-spreading river network.

Downstream from the Segre, the valley of the Ebro belongs more properly to Iberid Catalonia both as regards physical and human character.

The climate of this basin, surrounded as it is by enclosing mountains, is primarily continental in character and similar in many ways to that of the upper basin of the Guadalquivir. In winter the Ebro basin as a whole is covered by the continental high-pressure mass of outflowing air. In La Rioja Alta some cyclonic activity penetrates through the hills of eastern Asturias to bring a little frontal rain and thermal change, but elsewhere winter is a cool dry season. Mean monthly temperatures at Zaragoza and Lérida drop to under 50° F. between November and February. Cold descending air masses from the Iberian mountains produce sudden temperature drops to about 20° F., and January diurnal ranges may be as extreme as 40° F.—from 20° F. to 60° F. Apart, however, from the very damaging 'mistral' effects, winter thermal conditions are not ecologically very inhibitive. At higher altitudes temperature averages are lower and the winter longer, but diurnal ranges are less extreme.

In August mean temperatures rise to almost 80° F. in the lowlands of Lérida, they are slightly lower in the central basin and fall to 73° at Huesca.

Summer diurnal ranges of some 10–15° F. are not extreme but the suddenness of the temperature drop at nightfall can be a considerable physiological shock.

Rainfall is markedly concentrated in seasonal and detailed incidence, as well as being small in quantity. Zaragoza, typical of the Ebro lowlands, receives 11·5 ins. a year with a marked May maximum and a secondary peak in Autumn. Most of the precipitation is concentrated in a few rainy days, and is very unreliable in time and quantity. No part of the Ebro lowlands receives more than 15·5 ins. a year, but on the higher terraces bordering the Pyrenees rainfall rises to a little over 20 ins., e.g. Huesca, 21·5 ins. Aridity the whole year round is the dominating climatic factor, and only where irrigation water is available are crop-plants able to take advantage of the generally good thermal conditions.

Soil-formation and natural vegetation in the Ebro basin reflect a special relationship between contemporary climate and the underlying geology. In the first place there is the normal ecological and edaphic response—the formation of the dry nitrogenous and calcareous soils, and the cover of *monte bajo* (maquis) and woody bunch grasses so typical of eastern Spain. The softer clays form eroded and bare 'badlands', and the harder sandstones equally barren tabular hills. This type of landscape is confined to the upper slopes of the Ebro basin, and is neither to be found in the lowlands of the Ebro valley nor in the Cinca-Segre sub-region.

Along the flood plain of the Ebro (widest on thenor thern side downstream as far as the Cinca confluence) lies a broad alluvial belt which extends into the lower courses of the main tributaries. These generally calcified silts are fertile, easily worked, and have a relatively high water content.

Between the areas of alluvium and the mainly calcareous zones of the slightly more humid upper slopes lie the 'steppes' of the Ebro basin. Ecologically, these are quite distinct from the climatic steppes of La Mancha and of Murcia, in that they are associated with salinity. Downstream from Rioja Alta the Tertiary series includes considerable beds of salt and gypsum. The soluble salts available in the parent rocks have accumulated in the surface horizons as a result of vertical movement of the generally high water table. Saline efflorescences and pools are common in the whole region. Only by very careful application of irrigation water can the soils be leached of the soluble salts and made fit for cultivation; and in many areas even this is impossible. The natural vegetation of the steppe zone is severely restricted to halophytes as on the plains of Zaragoza and Lérida.

Of these three main ecological zones, only one, that of the alluviums and silts, is at all attractive to life. Even then considerable human effort has been required to overcome the problem of aridity. The harsh winter conditions inhibit citrus cultivation but the vine and olive flourish everywhere except on the badlands. Temperate tree-crops are debarred by aridity and the heat of summer.

On the 'secano'—land fit only for dry-farming—the main growing season is very short, limited by the relatively cold winter and baking-hot summer. Sown crops must therefore have a short cycle of rapid germination and maturation. Hard wheats of suitable varieties occupy about one-third of the cultivated area, a proportion roughly similar to that of Old Castile. 'Año y Vez' cultivation of alternate cereal and fallow is general, and the olive alone produces a continuous return from the land. In La Rioja Alta the slightly more suave and humid conditions allow the vine to flourish and this region is now the most important Spanish producer of marked wines, a good proportion of which go for export. The raising of fodder crops is extremely difficult, and livestock farming is confined to poor pastoralism associated with summer transhumant movement to Pyrenean and Iberian mountain pastures.

The irrigated zones—the 'huertas'—are very different. A narrow riverine belt around Zaragoza stretching along the Ebro and extending up the valley of the Jalón has been intensively irrigated and worked since Roman times. The alluvial silts on the north bank of the Ebro are naturally flood-irrigated by the left bank tributaries. To the south of the Ebro, the lesser volume of the Iberian rivers makes necessary the building of irrigation canals. The chief of these is the Imperial or Lodosa canal which leads off the Ebro some 15 miles down-stream of Logroño, and runs parallel to the river to a point 15 miles south-east of Zaragoza. The intervening tract has thus been made the richest part of the main Ebro basin, in which virtually all crops that flourish in Spain are grown. Frost damage can be considerable, and a major effort is needed to shelter and protect the sub-tropical exotics.

The second and most important irrigated area is that of the 'huertas' of Lérida. Here canals have been constructed to join the Cinca, Noguera and Segre rivers, water being led off to irrigate large interfluve areas covered with outwash silts. The scale of irrigation works is considerable, and the complexity of organisation is comparable with that of Valencia. No trust-worthy figures for irrigated areas are available, but around Lérida lands thus utilised extend over some 100,000–120,000 acres compared with 70,000 acres in the middle Ebro. Significantly, the only marked specialisation in the Cinco-Segre is of olive-growing, although where shelter against the cold winter winds be provided the whole range of sub-tropical crops can be raised.

In the Ebro depression there are thus demarcated four main human sub-regions: (i) the irrigated oases of the middle Ebro

valley and the Cinco-Segre basin, (ii) the Rioja Alta, intermediate between Navarre and the Ebro trough, (iii) the saline
steppes of the lower slopes, and (iv) the higher terracelands
such as those around Huesca.

The human response to general physical environment is un-
obscured by industrial development. Only to the east of Lérida
in historic Catalonia has there been recent economic change;
and even here developments have been slight.

On the higher terracelands below the Pyrenean foothills
relatively humid conditions enable fairly intensive cultivation
to be practised. Population density is high—over 100 per
square mile—and small- to medium-sized villages are thickly
scattered in a belt from Barbastro through Huesca to Tafalla.
In La Rioja Alta the numerous well-watered alluvial fans are
closely settled by an enterprising population who have vigorous Basque and Navarrese characteristics rather than the slow
dignity of Aragón. The small prosperous villages are very
reminiscent of the region around Santander. Logroño itself is
a sizable market town (population 58,500) of pre-Roman
origin. It serves as a commercial centre for the whole La Rioja
vine and orchard district and has an atmosphere and bustle
foreign to the Ebro region as a whole. It is significant that this
area has always been least valued by Aragón, and has always
led a comparatively independent existence.

The 'huertas' of Zaragoza carry the densest population con-
centrations to be found in the main Ebro basin. Settlement
consists of a ribbon of small riverside villages served by two
larger regional centres, Tudela and Zaragoza. Away from the
irrigated zone (which has population densities of between 200
and 300 per square mile) stretch almost uninhabited arid and
treeless plains and hills. The richness of the riverine lands is
thus rather exaggerated, and their climatic deficiencies obscured. Tudela and Zaragoza are fundamentally agricultural
centres, although the latter has always been of some route
importance. Lying half-way between Mediterranean and Atlantic Spain on a relatively easy routeway, Zaragoza is the
focus of routes from the Meseta and from Pyrenean Aragón.
To the east the Gallego valley leads up towards Huesca and

Jaca, breaking through the desolate middle-slope hills. To the west, the Jalón valley eroded in an uplifted Tertiary embayment in the Secondary Iberian ranges provides an easy and fertile route through the bleak highlands to the upper Henares and so to Madrid. From the upper Jalón at Calatayud fairly short mountain routes lead to Soria and the upper Douro, while, southwards via the Jiloca valley, run routes to Teruel and Valencia.

This convergence of topographically well-marked routes to all parts of eastern Spain has enabled Zaragoza to maintain its old Moorish pre-eminence. Good road and rail networks have increased its importance as a market centre, and encouraged the development of a variety of industries mainly concerned with the processing of agricultural products but also including metallurgical and engineering works. Its present population of 291,000, unlike that of many old centres such as Toledo, shows every sign of further increase and prosperity.

Lérida, the centre of the second oasis region, is more akin to Logroño than to Zaragoza. Its population of some 67,000 is mainly concerned with serving the Segre-Cinca basin. With no great positional advantage after the conclusion of the three-cornered struggle between Aragón, Catalonia and the Moslem kingdoms, it has remained a rural town with a few processing industries.

The Ebro valley east of the confluence of the Cinca-Segre river is noteworthy for the absence of any important settlements. In the relatively narrow valley, unimportant as a routeway before the coming of the railroad to Tortosa, a string of small rural towns huddle along the restricted river terraces, all of approximately equal importance. Here Mediterranean influences are strongest, and links with the Ebro basin are relatively weak.

As noted earlier, away from the 'huertas' and below the upper terracelands stretch the great Ebro flats. Scorched in summer, desiccated and often frozen by bleak winter winds, the dry sandstone hills, eroded clays and poor saline steppes make up over half of the total area of the Ebro basin. Still very sparsely populated, these great negative areas must have appeared extraordinarily uninviting even to the peoples of the high Pyrenees, let alone to the Catalan coastal groups. Here is to be found the main reason for the slowness of the expansion of the Christian kingdoms of the East. Here too is found the explanation for the slow natural partitioning of the old Kingdom of Aragón. From the end of the 15th century onwards, the main Ebro basin became more and more assimilated into Meseta Castile, while Catalonia returned to its old Mediterranean individuality.

THE IBERIAN MOUNTAINS

Of all the main rivers of northern Spain the Ebro alone does not rise in the Iberian mountains. This great highland mass, which stretches from the mountains of Asturias to within a short distance of the Mediterranean, is a natural divide of considerable importance. These mountains shut off the Meseta from the main European land-mass in many ways more effectively than do the Pyrenees. Physiographic, biological, ethnographic and cultural barriers, they have allowed Castile to develop in relatively inviolate isolation.

These Iberian mountains are now generally regarded as being part of a system of Tertiary Foreland folding that developed between the true Alpine folding of the Betic Cordillera and the rigid Archean central block. This main Iberide upwarping and folding of Secondary and early Tertiary rocks extends from Burgos to Valencia, and transversely from the Sierra Morena to the Catalan hills (inclusive).

The underlying Palaeozoic series were heavily faulted; and elevated blocks are now exposed in the Sierra Demanda and Sierra del Moncayo. Secondary rocks form the general substratum, intermittently exposed by later erosion, the Cretaceous beds being of considerable regional importance—as round Cuenca. These older rocks form two distinct folded belts aligned north-west to south-east, between which less resistant Tertiary beds are dominant. One of these belts stretches from the plateau edge behind Valencia, through the Montes Universales to Medinaceli on the watershed between the Henares and the Jalón. The second rises in the mountains overlooking Burgos, and runs east of the uplifted Tertiary basins of Soria and Calatayud in the Sierra del Moncayo and Sierra de Vicor. In the province of Teruel this Mesozoic belt fans out, overlooking the Jiloca valley from the east and the Ebro depression from the west, first rising to form the high sierras of Gúdar and then curving round to join the Catalan hills.

Between these two old rock belts lying 'en echelon', a series of structural depressions floored by Tertiary and Recent sedimentaries have been further lowered by river erosion. In these depressions settlement has concentrated, and along the river-formed valleys a network of major routeways has developed.

The relief of the uplands above 10,000 ft. shows considerable variety. Alpine glaciation has everywhere left its mark, and frost action still fashions jagged peaks and narrow arêtes in the high sierras. Elsewhere, differential erosion of crystalline, metamorphic and sedimentary rocks has produced a variety of terrains. Dominating all are the Jurassic and Cretaceous limestone 'Paramos'. These are high and barren plateaux deeply incised by torrent valleys, sometimes fantastically wind eroded, as at La Ciudad Encantada, (the Enchanted City), above Cuenca.

The Tertiary basins of, for example, Teruel and Calatayud appear as oases of less savage terrain. The former lies on narrow forested terrace-lands at an altitude of 3000 ft., surrounded by eroded red clay hills. The latter, at a height of 1750 ft., is sited in a narrow clay depression—much of it eroded badland, only attractive in comparison to the bleak mountains above. The Soria basin (of low dissected hills of a variety of Tertiary rocks) is of considerable extent, and though remote has since the pre-Roman days of Numantia supported a considerable population.

The weather experienced in this region emphasises the structural and topographic subdivisions. The climate is continental in character, varying in severity with altitude. Molina de Aragón (altitude 3400 ft.) has a typical upland régime. Minimum temperatures lower than 32° F. have been recorded for every month except August and the extreme minimum of

— 17° F. is the lowest recorded in Spain. Mean monthly temperatures of below 41° F. are recorded for the five months November to April, and the average diurnal range exceeds 30° F. Summer means rise to 68° but the daily range also increases to between 45° F. daily minimum and 95–100° F. daily maximum. Mountain winds, cold and desiccating, are experienced the year round. Annual rainfall averages on these southern uplands are about 18 ins., falling in spring and autumn rainstorms and as prolonged winter snow-showers.

Thermal conditions are less extreme in the basins. Soria and Teruel have two months without frost, and have the same recorded minimum temperature of — 4° F. Average winter diurnal ranges are less than 25° F. Summer means vary with distance from the sea rather than with altitude. The depressions also have lower rainfall, falling to about 15 ins. in the south and 18 ins. in the north.

In all, the climate and weather of this region is the most repellent to be found in Spain. The aridity of summer, and cold severity of a long winter greatly limit plant growth and soil development. The limestone 'Paramos' add edaphic poverty to climatic difficulty.

The lignites of Montalban and Aliaga, which produce over one-third of the Spanish production of brown coal, are of little absolute economic importance and the small Carboniferous coalbeds of the Sierra Demanda are of even less value (total annual production in coal equivalent is approximately 23,000 tons). The peoples of the Iberian mountains are thus almost completely dependent on their very poor land resources. The carrying capacity for flocks or for cultivation is extremely low, and population very sparse. Great tracts are completely uninhabited, and even in the relatively fertile Soria basin population density is less than 40 per square mile. Rainfall deficiency, bleak winds and the difficulty of obtaining water on the predominantly limestone uplands have driven settlement into sheltered spring-like depressions.

The only settlements with populations of over 10,000 are those sited at nodal points in the central Tertiary belt. Here, as in Old Castile, the route towns are driven down from the bleak passes to less commanding but more fertile situations. One line of towns lies between the two old rock zones, controlling the route Valencia–Teruel–Calatayud–Soria–Burgos. Calatayud and Soria lie on the shortest transverse passes of the Iberian mountains, the former on a line between Zaragoza, Madrid and Almazán, the latter, from its large depression communicating with Burgos, the upper Douro, the Henares, Calatayud, Tudela and Logroño. Cuenca (a basin or depression) has always been important for its control from the north of the Júcar corridor.

These route alignments are vastly more important than any other factor in the human geography of the region. The Iberian mountain regions lives on activity originating outside, rather than on any indigenous resources. Through them pass peoples and ideas, but never do these take root. From the narrow Mediterranean littoral which they overlook so grimly, these highlands really appear the abomination of desolation. It is by no means strange that they were so easily and permanently adopted as the divide between the kingdoms of Castile and Aragón.

CATALONIA

In terms of everything but landscapes, Catalonia is extraordinarily difficult to define. Catalan speech may be heard everywhere east of a line Maladeta–Valencia–Alicante. The historic kingdom of Catalonia was contained in a triangle Roussillon–Maladeta–Tortosa. Modern industrial Catalonia is essentially Barcelona province. In physical and directly observable terms we may take it to include first the coastlands between the French frontier and Alcalá, and secondly the hills that lie between the Cinca-Segre basin and the coastlands. This is the area always indisputably attached to Barcelona rather than to Aragón or Valencia, and above all the most Frankish part of the Spanish Levante.

Structurally this region is related to the Iberian mountains.

Tertiary tectonic action here produced south-west to north-east aligned folding of Archean, Palaeozoic and Mesozoic rocks that made up an Alpine foreland. This great wall of mountains extended westward into the Iberian Sierra de Gúdar, and was later cut through by the Ebro which during Oligo-Miocene times was dammed up in an interior depression. During the Tertiary upheaval Archean granites of the basal Iberian platform were elevated and faulted, and now survive in the Sierra de Montseny, locally termed Montseny Sencillamente—the plain or simple hills because of their bare rounded outlines.

Structurally and topographically the most significant feature is the longitudinal arrangement of coastal mountains, an interior depression, and the innermost Catalan hills. The hill-belt of the littoral rises from the sea at Cape Mongo on the south side of Rosas Bay, and, broken only by transverse river valleys, runs parallel to the coast to within 20 miles of Tarragona. Between this point and the Ebro it disappears, only to re-emerge across the Ebro delta and continue as a series of disconnected hills to Alcalá. These coastal sierras rise steeply from the sea to an average altitude of just over 1500 ft.; although at Montnegro and to the north-east of Barcelona they tower up to 3000 ft. Formed in the main of old crystalline rocks and Mesozoic limestones, these coastal hills (although easily penetrated along the numerous transverse valleys) have always been a negative belt. The coastal lowlands, almost non-existent along the Costa Brava, and widest around the deltaic mouths of the Ter, Llobregat and Ebro, have until recently been orientated seaward—away from the dry infertile hills farther inland. Only with industrial growth have Barcelona, Mataró and the other coastal settlements developed interests in the immediate interior.

Behind the coast ranges lies a parallel depression which opens on to the coast, at the Gulf of Rosas in the plain of Ampurdán in the north, and in the Tarragona 'huerta' in the south. Alluvial infilling of this mainly tectonic depression has submerged all but a few Tertiary residual hills, to form a long narrow undulating inner basin. Between Tarragona and the

Ebro this depression forms a hilly coastal plain, in which calcareous Tertiary rocks are exposed. Both here and in the smaller depression south of the Ebro the incoming streams rise in the narrowest sections of the Catalan-Iberian mountains, and the alluvial infill is thin and discontinuous. In this area the main difference emerges between the northern coastal 'huertas', watered by the rivers of the Pyrenees and pluviose Spain; and those south of Alcalá supplied by the streams of the Meseta—and of strictly Mediterranean régime.

These two zones of the coastal ranges and the interior depression form the sub-region here termed the Catalan Coastlands.

To the interior lies the folded belt of the Catalan hills which, broken only by the Manresa basin, extends from the Ebro northwards into the Pyrenees. West of the Llobregat, Jurassic limestones predominate in the dissected hill-land which lies at a general level of some 1800 ft. South-west–north-east aligned sierras rise above to over 3300 ft., but this inner hill belt is in no way to be regarded as a serious topographic barrier between the littoral and the interior. East of the Llobregat the Catalan hills are both higher and wider but overshadowed by the Pyrenean cordilleras into which they merge. The boundary between the Catalan hill region and that of the Pyrenees is marked by a landscape change from Mediterranean calcareous hills through a narrow outwash piedmont zone stretching eastwards from Castellalt to humid forested mountains. North of the Ter, Tertiary volcanic activity responsible for the Olot basin and surrounding hills marks the contact zone between the two great fold systems of the Pyrenees and the Iberian-Catalan ranges.

Climatic conditions emphasise the tripartite structural and topographic division of this region. A Mediterranean régime is characteristic of the whole area, but in the Catalan hills there is a transition to the continental conditions of the Ebro basin on the one hand, and to the mountain climates of the lower Pyrenees on the other.

The Coastlands are to some extent affected during winter by cold air moving from the interior into the Mediterranean cyclone zone. This movement becomes progressively weaker southwards along the coast; Barcelona being occasionally affected by 'mistral' type winds from the Pyrenees and recording an absolute minimum of 14° F., compared with 21° F. at Valencia. Mean monthly temperatures are high, falling below 50° F. only during December and January and rising to 77° F. during the summer. In this north-eastern coastal region maritime influences are dominant, producing small thermal ranges —less than 9° F., diurnal and seasonal. Maximum temperatures very rarely rise above 90° F.

Mean temperatures tend to be slightly lower in the hill-lands, although the western flanks of the Catalan hills experience altitude-modified hot summers characteristic of the Ebro basin. The longitudinal depression is shut off from the sea winds, and while summer temperatures are actually only a little higher than on the coast, the hot still air is much more oppressive.

Rainfall averages over 25 ins. per annum on the Costa Brava, rises to over 40 ins. in the mountains around Olot, and falls to 16 ins. or less south of Tortosa. In the coastlands, well-marked autumn and spring maxima appear; although to the north of the Ebro mean monthly readings illustrate the maritime modification of the Mediterranean régime—January and February minima 1·2 ins., April maximum 2 ins., October 3 ins. Unlike the southern littoral and the interior, the coastlands do not experience absolute summer drought—though variability is considerable south of Tortosa. In the north irrigation is desirable but not intensively developed; to the south it becomes essential and widespread.

The hill-lands, although they have slightly heavier total precipitation, have a smaller effective rainfall. Slight latitudinal differences appear in that north of Vich winter cloudiness and number of rain days are both fairly high. In general, the permeability of the surface rocks, thinness of soils and vegetation cover all reduce the effectiveness of precipitation that is by no means really heavy. Humidity decreases rapidly inland, and the shelving hills overlooking the Lérida basin are extremely arid.

The hydrography is thus determined by the width and character of the hill-zone, and its proximity to the Pyrenees. The only large rivers of the Llobregat and Ter systems derive most of their water from the rain and snows of the Sierra del Cadi and Canigou. Thus fed, they break transversely through the parallel ranges, bringing (particularly in spring and early summer) considerable quantities of silt to form great deltaic plains. The Ebro, fed similarily by its northern tributaries, breaks through the Iberide chain to form a great bird's foot delta, at the head of which lies Tortosa. Those streams which rise in the Catalan hills and the eastern part of the Iberian mountains have much smaller volume and intermittent flow, and are very prone to sudden torrential floods.

The first group of rivers have cut great valleys through the backing sierras, and the relative isolation of the Catalan coastlands from the interior is of choice rather than necessity. Here too where the climate is most bland, and rainfall heaviest and most assured, the rivers have added their water supply and alluvium.

The shorter rivers of Mediterranean régime (and this is true also of the whole south-eastern littoral), are much less able to ameliorate through water-supply and alluvial infill the more difficult topographic and climatic conditions. The valleys are narrower, of steeper gradient and vulnerable to flood; and are hence avoided by communications.

This distinction is of some importance in explaining the rise of Barcelona, and the growth of numerous urban and industrial centres contrasted with the comparative stagnation of the other lands of the Levante. As noted below, Catalonia now draws food and water-supplies from well outside the region, but for millennia it has been the region best endowed not only for population growth but for economic progress. South of Tarragona, settlement is almost entirely rural—even in Valencia city many of the dwellings are really farmhouses—and has restricted economic and social functions. Northwards, even the smaller towns of the coastland sub-region have a variety of activities; and attention has never had to be confined to intensive exploitation of limited natural resources.

Catalonia is in other ways remarkably poor in resources. In the upper Llobregat basin some 70,000 tons of lignite are produced annually and in the nearby Cardoner valley 20 miles north of Manresa lie large deposits of sodium and potassic salts. No other significant mineral deposits exist. Agricultural resources are, however, considerable, and settlement (with the exception of Barcelona) developed until recently on a rural basis.

A genial climate makes possible the cultivation of the whole range of temperate and sub-tropical tree-crops in the lowlands. On the crystalline and limestone hills local soil factors and shortage of water make cultivation virtually impossible, except in sheltered pockets of Terra Rossa. Along the Costa Brava the narrowness of the coastal plain, and the strong sea-winds tend to limit cultivation to the hardier tree-crops such as the olive and vine. The main distinction between the agricultural characteristics of the two sub-regions appears as follows. In the Catalan hills intensive cultivation is confined to the river valleys, above which lie poor pastures and scrub forest—the highland aspect is dominant. In the Coastlands, intensive cultivation laps around the coastal sierras on all sides and breaks through from littoral to inner depression in many places; here the lowlands are dominant.

Some regional specialisation is observable. Catalonia is the most important vine-producing region of Spain, measured by value of product. This pre-eminence largely results from climatic and geological factors. The Palaeozoic rocks contribute a much prized bouquet to the wines of Priorato west of Montsant, and of Reus. Everywhere east of the main watershed, a relatively genial climate without extremes raises yields and quality to a high level. On the hills around Gerona cork trees have given rise to a local industry, while on the saline shores of the Gulf of Rosas and the Ebro delta rice-growing is of local importance. Of greatest significance in the region as a whole is market gardening of vegetables. The very large urban concentration of population has produced regional markets for foodstuffs which have revolutionised agriculture. With the solitary exception of specialised viticulture for export, practically all agricultural products are raised for consumption in the nearby industrial towns.

This agglomeration is by far the most important in Spain. The region as a whole has a population of some two and a half millions, half of which live in Barcelona. In the western Panadés, on the irrigated Campo de Tarragona and Llobregat delta, intensive mixed agriculture supports a population density of 400 people per square mile. The lowlands of Ampurdán, the inner depression and the littoral have densities of over 300, an intensity also found in the sheltered vine-growing basins around Reus and Falset. The lowest population densities are found in the interior-facing Catalan hills, and on the unirrigated littoral south of the Ebro.

With the exception of Barcelona, all settlements originated as defensively sited nuclear centres for rural or fishing activities. The spread of dispersed settlement away from the old centres into the lowlands is relatively recent, and is still actively proceeding in the Ebro delta. Where (as along the Costa Brava and near Garraf) defensive siting has resulted in inaccessibility, the downward spread of population has been accompanied by the abandonment of the older villages. Elsewhere, the old sites have become centres of increasingly prosperous districts and have benefited accordingly.

This change, inevitable even in a purely agricultural society, was accelerated by industrialisation.

In Roman times Emporium on the Gulf of Rosas was noted for its weaving of flax grown in the Ebro basin. Barcino, a pre-Roman settlement, was at first rivalled by Tarraco (Tarragona), the centre of a highly-rated wine-producing area, but gradually assumed the leadership, first as a colonia and later as a seaport. Captured by the Moors in 713 and named Bardjaluna, it became after the Frankish reconquest in 801 the centre of the Spanish Mark. With the virtual independence of its Counts at the end of the 9th century, Barcelona developed once more an independent commercial life. Until 1474 it remained little more than an open roadstead; and not until the 17th century was a harbour built. Nevertheless by the end of the 13th century it had become one of the foremost trading cities of the world. The 'Libre del Consulat de Mar', the Catalan maritime code of the 13th century, and the Catalan Atlas óf Portolani charts dating from 1375, are supreme examples of skill in maritime affairs.

The development of Barcelona as a commercial centre has to be understood both in terms of site and general location. The port lies between the deltas of the rivers Llobregat and Besos, distant enough from the river mouths to avoid the rapid silting up which destroyed Emporium and its neighbour Rhode but sufficiently near to utilise the valley routeways into the interior. Between 801 and the late 13th century, Barcelona was the westernmost Christian held port in the Mediterranean. While Venice, Genoa and Pisa traded with the eastern Mediterranean, Barcelona developed a trading empire in the west with Christian and Moslem alike. The hinterland supplied wine and wool, but the port produced not only textiles but iron-ware, glass, jewellery, pottery as well as marine supplies. Industry developed from commercial contact rather than on local resources, although local agricultural wealth alone made possible rapid urban growth.

The union of Aragon with Castile, and the favouring of Castilian ports that followed resulted in the decline in importance of Barcelona, a decline that in any case inevitably followed the discovery of the New World and a change in world economic affairs. Not until the mid-18th century were trading restrictions removed, and industries encouraged. From that time onward the city itself grew and its multifarious activities spread into neighbouring settlements. Barcelona, with a population of over 1,600,000, is exceeded in size only by Madrid. Around it lies a constellation of industrial towns. Tarrasa and Sabadell in Vallés possess between them over half the wool-working capacity of Spain. The former has a population of 59,000; the latter, 105,000. Manresa (40,000), in the Llobregat valley, and Igualada on the Noya are both

route-towns and leather, woollen and cotton centres. Bada-
lona (62,000) is now an industrialised suburb of Barcelona.
Mataró (32,000), an old fishing port, has become a ship-
building and textile centre. This nuclear region of the province
of Barcelona now draws hydro-electricity and water from the
Cinca-Segre basin, and raw materials and foodstuffs from the
whole world. The industrial population has also largely been
drawn from outside the region—in 1930 only one-half of the
inhabitants of Barcelona had been born either in the city or
the region.

Away from this main urban constellation, two main areas
of growth are observable. To the north Gerona (population
29,000) is the provincial centre of a fertile rural lowland and a
focus for communications along the Ter valley, from the Olot
basin, and of the Ampurdán lowland. In the south Tarragona
has remained the port and commercial centre for an agricultural region, and its functions are more akin to those of
Málaga and Valencia than to Barcelona. Tortosa, situated
originally for security in the Ebro gorge, 9 miles upstream
from the deltaic lowland, has not dissimilar functions. Unimportant both as a port and route centre, Tortosa is essentially a rural market centre for the 'huerta' area downstream.

Culturally and in the landscape there are then three Cata-
lonias. The first is characterised by hill and basin cultivation
of the olive and vine, by Montes Bajo and fretted limestone.
The second Catalonia is marked by general and intensive cultivation of lowland 'huertas'. The third is that of bustling
Barcelona, not so much Catalan as cosmopolitan. Historically
these three component parts have always been in conflict,
combining then as now only in restless dislike of Castilian
control.

Chapter 12

CENTRAL SPAIN

THE Central Sierras are a series of highland ranges of south-west–north-east alignment that, arranged in echelon, stretch from the Portuguese frontier to the Iberian mountains, separating the basins of the Douro and Tagus. Composed in the main of uplifted basal granites, these sierras vary considerably in altitude and in their barrier nature.

The Sierra de Gata in the west is an area of dissected terrain in which isolated mountains rise to over 3000 ft. in height. This area is merely an elevated portion of the granite block of western Old Castile, North Portugal and Galicia. In the central section the de Gredos range (with an average altitude of over 5000 ft., rising at Picos de Almansor to 8500), grimly overlooks the 1000-ft.-high lands of the middle Tagus. On the northern flank, the Paramera, less rugged but bleak moorland, little of which lies at over 5000 ft., drops less precipitously down from the Sierra de Ávila to the high table-land of Old Castile.

Between the roughly parallel ranges run long tectonic depressions of great importance for communications. Plasencia lies at the southern entrances of two of these depressions, routes to Salamanca and to Avila forking either side of the Tras la Sierra mountains.

East of the Sierra de Gredos lies another col region. Connecting Old and New Castile are three main passes with significantly different characteristics. The western pass as its name 'La Cañada' indicates was long of importance to migratory shepherds. In spite of its low altitude (4500 ft.) it is now only used by the Madrid railway to the north-west. A steep ascent on its southern flank is followed by a long traverse of mountain country suitable enough for sheep pasture but not productive of much traffic. The eastern pass of Navacerrada is the shortest route between Madrid and Segovia. But although its mountain section is shorter than 'La Cañada', it is 5800 ft. high, and hence only carries a secondary road through the eastern Sierra de Guadarrama.

Of most present importance is the central pass of Guadarrama lying between the Sierra de Malagón and the Guadarramas. Gradients are not extreme and the mountain traverse short. A main road and railway now use this route between Madrid and the middle Tagus lands.

To the east of this col region rises the Sierra de Guadarrama which, wide and unbroken, runs north-eastward to merge into the Iberian mountains. Crossed only in one place by the Madrid–Burgos 'Carratera Nacional' which, soon to be paralleled by a railway, crosses the pass of Somosierra at 5800 ft., the Guadarramas form a real barrier to movement. Their considerable height and extent—a belt 70 miles long and between 5 and 10 miles wide rising to 5500 ft.—produces a great negative zone interposed between Old and New Castile.

Climatic conditions are harsh. Orographical effects increase precipitation above the Meseta norm to between 20 ins. and 30 ins. a year. Instability rainfall, heaviest on the northern flanks, has an early summer maximum and secondary autumn peak. Snowfall is recorded for every month except June, July and August, resulting in blocked passes and the isolation of the upland basins.

Temperatures reach Castilian extremes, and in general the relatively gradual northern slopes are colder than the steeper southern flanks.

Soils are acid and thin, and vegetation cover, mainly of wet scrub-forest, impoverished by centuries of over-grazing. Some pinewoods of importance survive in the Guadarramas, and summer alpine pasture is still valued and used in the eastern half of this region.

Unlike the Sierra Morena, the Central Sierras have no significant mineral wealth, and the population of the region is

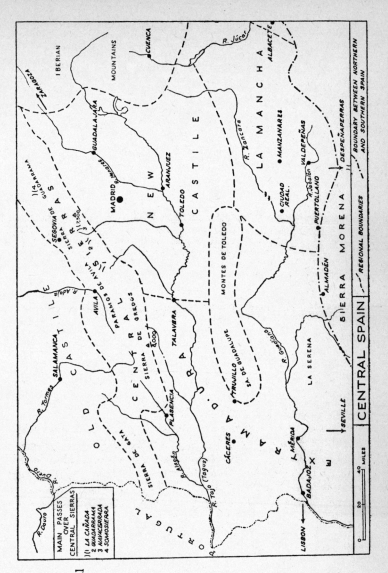

16 Central Spain

therefore concentrated in the upland valleys and along the foothills. The remoter of the mountain basins such as that of Las Hurdes lying under the Sierra de Gata are areas of poverty-stricken hamlets. Those villages lying on main routes —as that between Plasencia and Ávila—are slightly more prosperous, while in the Guadarrama mountains a small-scale tourist and holiday industry is slowly developing.

As in the Iberian mountains, this region with an average population density of 30 per square mile and large stretches completely uninhabited, is entirely dependent on activity originating outside its boundaries. Fortunately it is by no means as insuperable a barrier region as is often supposed.

THE SOUTHERN MESETA

Between the Central Sierras and the Sierra Morena, the Portuguese frontier and the Mediterranean coastal lowlands, lies the southern Meseta of Central Spain. Before examining its component regions it is worthwhile considering its physical character as a whole.

Geologically it falls into two halves. East of Talavera and of Ciudad Real the basins of the Tagus and Guadiana are part of a Tertiary-floored depression structurally similar to that of Old Castile. In the threshold region of the Júcar this depression extends to within sight of the lower Tertiary basin of Valencia. Westwards the Meseta is composed of exposed sedimentary and crystalline Palaeozoic rocks, which, peneplained at an early phase, are now deeply incised by the lower Tagus and Guadiana. Around Badajoz on the Guadiana lies a more open Tertiary basin that partly explains the site of the city. The old Hercynian-folded rocks are fringed on the north-east by a long tongue of exposed granites rooted in the Sierra de Estrella, and which extend across the Tagus. Along the junction of Archean and Palaeozoic rocks rise the Sierra de Guadelupe and the Montes de Toledo.

Topographically the whole region is one of subdued relief broken only by the western gorges of the Atlantic-flowing rivers and the dissected hills of the transverse sierras, which rarely rise over 3000 ft. The variations in relief have been determined in the main by differential erosion. Triassic limestones form the karstlands of La Mancha, Tertiary sands and clays the mesa country of New Castile, whilst on the harder Palaeozoics occur the broken flats of Extramadura.

Ecologically the lands of the southern Meseta are lands of harshness and poverty. Flora and fauna are restricted in number and variety, resources for human life few. Everywhere over what has been called the 'military landscape' broods a desolation that is fascinating in its grandeur.

NEW CASTILE

This is essentially the Tertiary basin of the Tagus downstream to Talavera. Rarely rising over 1800 ft. lies an old erosion surface, giving a generally 'senile' landscape. Steeply to the north, more gradually to the east, mountain chains overlook Old Castile. To the west a decrease in altitude is accompanied by an increase in ruggedness. To the south-east the watershed between the Tagus and the Guadiana is a zone of southward increasing flatness.

Tertiary deposits, of which Miocene lacustrine beds are most important, retain their original horizontality, thus adding structural flatness to the planation of erosive forces. Residual hills usually capped by limestones form tabular hills which, in vivid greys, reds, violets and blues of the various outcrops stand out strikingly above the red-brown flats. Goya captured some of their landscape effect when he sketched them as crouching fantastic beasts.

The Tagus and its northern tributary systems have built up large alluvial fans where they emerge from the mountains; and on these silts and the alluvium of the broad but incised floodplains lie the better farmlands. Southern tributaries are small and few, and have made little impression on the landscape either by erosion or deposition. The river régimes are strikingly continental in character, flow varying from a winter maximum through sudden and torrential spring snow-melt floods in the north to dispirited summer trickles. Cervantes was but the most famous of the scoffers at the Manzanares when he wrote of 'a rivulet with the pretensions of a river'. This great fluctuation in flow has vastly increased the difficulty of the generation of hydro-electricity, so necessary to a region that possesses the largest town in Spain and practically no fuel.

The climate is an extreme form of that of Old Castile, except that altitudinal effects on temperature are less marked. At Madrid mean monthly temperatures average under 41° F. during December and January, and the diurnal range lies between 20° F. and 55° F., the lowest recorded temperature being 8·5° F. Bleak mountain winds can cause sudden and considerable drops in temperature. In summer intense insolation brings a rapid thermal increase, mean monthly temperatures rising above 68° F. between June and September. The diurnal temperature range also rises to between 50° F. and 100° F., and Madrid has several times recorded over 110° F. Even in summer, cold descending air from the Central Sierras often suddenly and extremely lowers day temperatures—we may recall from an earlier chapter 'a wind that will not flutter a candle . . .'

Precipitation is in total little less than in the lowlands of Old Castile, but its seasonal distribution is more extreme. Madrid (with 16·5 ins. a year) has more rainfall than has Valladolid, but this largely results from the more prolonged and stormy autumn maximum—2 ins. in November—and conceals the much longer dry hot summer experienced by New Castile. Most serious is the unreliability of precipitation, which is the real cause of frequent drought.

Soils are predominantly of dry calcareous type, although clay and gypsum outcrops provide considerable variants. Chemically rich, although with a low organic content, most soils are mechanically weak and very vulnerable to erosion. The frequency of bare-fallowing, and the thin summer cover even of natural vegetation allow the heavy storm rains to have very destructive effects on the soil mantle. Natural vegetation is xerophytic, composed mainly of woody grasses, tubers and scrub forest with dry oak. In winter a flush of annuals produces winter pasture alongside the green cultivated wheatfields. In summer the *calina* heat haze hangs over bare red-brown soil, the grey of olive trees, and thyme dominated *matorral*.

Agricultural resources, which constitute the sole wealth of the Tertiary basin of New Castile, are limited. Well-watered fertile land is confined to the alluvial valley floors and the finer silts of the outwash fans. The incised character of the valleys restricts irrigation to narrow riverine belts, and whenever the confluence of streams produces a widening of this belt intensive cultivation forms marked oases, for example around Aranjuez and in the Alberche valley. These sheltered lowlands carry vines, vegetable and fruit crops mainly for the Madrid market.

The tableland proper is only capable of carrying rapidly growing plants of low water requirements, and drought resisting tree crops. Durum wheats and barley alone are of general importance. Water-conserving fallow periods are long, the 'año y vez' of alternate cereal and fallow often being displaced by the even less productive 'al tercio'—one crop in every three years. Yields over a term of years are low, and fluctuations considerable. Apart from barley grown mainly for work animals, forage and fodder are desperately short. Sheep, the only stock widely distributed, are entirely dependent on the poor winter pasture of those areas too barren to cultivate and on fallow stubble. Since the 13th century rise of the Mesta, the interests of sedentary farmers have conflicted with those of the migrant herders, only triumphing within the last century. A stable arrangement, by which arable land would benefit from fallow-folding and the flocks find forage, has yet to be evolved.

Population density, as might be expected, is low, averaging less than 50 per square mile on the 'secano' and rising to over 100 only along the Tagus and the lower courses of its northern tributaries. Devastated during the last stages of the Reconquista and reoccupied mainly under military feudalism, New Castile is a region of widely separated 'settlement' villages. Seeking water and shelter, these adobe clusters huddle in small depressions, and in the shadow of the mesas. The Mesta migrant flocks which used to traverse the region along the de la Mancha and Segoviana 'Cañadas' were also responsible for preventing dispersal of settlement.

Of the individual towns, Madrid (which now contains over half of the population of New Castile) is the most recently established. Toledo, which stands on a defensible hill site 300 ft. above the Tagus, was a pre-Roman fortified centre. Until 1087 it increased its eminence under various rulers because of its military value in spite of the congestion of the hilltop site. In the Moorish period it became a centre of learning and trade, its manufacture of high grade steel for weapons being based on charcoal and iron from the nearby Montes de Toledo. After the Reconquest the detailed inadequacies of its difficult site and the relative poverty of its hinterland became more obvious—here the Tagus flows in a deep gorge and the broken terrain is more difficult to cultivate than the table-lands proper. Aranjuez has more fertile land, and Madrid had the Court and room for expansion.

Aranjuez and Guadalajara are now primarily market towns for lowland farming zones. The former has derived little benefit from its river-crossing, mainly because the routes running south and south-eastward from Madrid led to even poorer Meseta areas. Only in recent years has the connection between the Levante and the capital become important. Guadalajara lies on the busier Henares-Jalón route but, like all the other centres, owes relative stagnation to the overwhelming growth of the capital. Talavera, apart from being the gateway to poor northern Extramadura and possessing a famous porcelain manufacture, is similarly a provincial market town.

Madrid, which is now the largest city of Spain (population 2,500,000), has grown from humble origins. It lies on open table-lands at a height of 2000 ft., at the confluence of two small rivers, off the old main routeways of the Guadarrama and Henares valleys. Early a fortified outpost of Toledo, it grew as a rural frontier town and one of the Court centres. This sudden growth of a fortune, which although fluctuating has survived, is in a sense strange. The frequently quoted analogy with the site of Berlin is misleading, since the latter has many positive advantages while Madrid has only centrality and space.

It should be remembered that Charles V, who used Madrid very frequently as a centre of imperial operations, and Philip II who finally established the capital, were Habsburgs of Flemish background. They had no especial regard for any particular Spanish region; and indeed it was to their advantage not to antagonise any of the old kingdoms by favouring one of them. Having no regional ties, accustomed to think on an imperial scale, they chose a remote but central, provincial and free new town. Thenceforward Madrid grew rapidly—first as a centre for the Court and administration, and later more slowly as an industrial centre processing imported raw materials for its own consumption. Since the 18th century it has grown on its unrestricted site like any other capital.

In so doing it stultified the growth of its old rivals, drawing to itself most of the people and wealth of New Castile. Madrid now lies at the centre of a great concentric web of communications. So often is it quicker in travelling between the peripheral regions to strike inland to the capital and then again outward than to attempt a direct route that, more truly than of Rome, can it be said that all roads lead to Madrid.

LA MANCHA

South-eastwards from New Castile over the low and ill-defined watershed between the upper valleys of the Tagus and the Guadiana lies La Mancha, the country of Don Quixote.

Structurally, this region forms the southern half of the double basin of Tertiary southern Meseta. Topographically it is quite different from New Castile. Between the high sierras of the Iberian mountains and the Betic Cordillera lies a high 'senile' monotonous plateau, seldom relieved by any change in gradient. Lying at an altitude of 2000 ft., this table-land is sluggishly traversed by the Záncara and Jabalón tributaries of the Guadiana. Gradients are so slight that streams stagnate in seasonally dry creeks and lagoons—incidentally thus making the windmills against which the Don tilted necessary for corn-grinding.

The surface rocks are mainly Triassic limestone, and surface drainage is largely discontinuous between swallow-holes and springs. Barren karst covers much of the higher land, while everywhere soil formation is slow. In the depressions where the water table is fairly near the surface, water can be obtained from shallow wells. Where the water table seasonally rises to the surface, ephemeral marshes and salt-pans result; and later evaporation of surface water forms areas of saline steppe. These saline steppes differ from those of the Ebro basin in that climatic rather than geological effects predominate.

Climatic conditions are the most extreme to be found on the Meseta. Winter temperatures are a little higher than in New Castile, but cold winds sweep continuously across the bare plains. Extreme summer temperatures are no higher than in Madrid, but the diurnal range is greater and the brassy heat less broken by cold winds. Annual rainfall rarely exceeds 14 ins., variability is high, and precipitation effectiveness reduced by rapid percolation and evaporation. Climatic and soil aridity is the mark of La Mancha.

Agriculture, the only economic activity, is severely restricted by these difficult environmental conditions. Hard short-cycle wheats, barley and oats are grown monoculturally on the open plains. The cultivation of red oats is significant, in that as rye is an indicator of leached acid soils in rainy Spain so southern oats, a fair crop of which can be raised by any farmer on any land, indicate the presence of hazardous dry conditions. In those calcareous areas where the water table is reasonably high or where well supplies are good, and in depressions sheltered from desiccating winds, the vine is supreme. La Mancha has the greatest area devoted to viticulture of any region of Spain but yields are low and quality inferior. With double the Catalan acreage, La Mancha produces the same quantity of wine of about half the value, most of it being blended with wines of the Levante. Valdepeñas and the Campo de Calatrava, stretching away to Ciudad Real, owe the superior quality of their product to mixed soils of volcanic,

Palaeozoic and Recent parent rocks. Olives are only important on the western margin of La Mancha on the old-rock hills. Wild esparto grass, once extensively harvested in the saline steppe areas, is no longer of great importance, the cultivated crops of the Levante having largely captured the markets.

The harshness of environment has made this an area of repulsion to settlement. Once important during the Reconquista for the approach from New Castile to the pass of Despeñaperros and so to Andalusia, La Mancha is now a forgotten region. Calatrava, once the strong point of a famous military order and the centre of great winter sheep pastures from which ran the Cañada de la Mancha north to Cuenca and Soria, is now but a name. Ciudad Real, founded in 1252 at a point where the Guadiana leaves the Tertiary upland to enter the wetter and hillier country of Extramadura, is little more than a large market town. Valdepeñas, once merely the centre for a rural area more fertile than the plains to the north-east, has developed rapidly as a route centre in recent years. Added to its 'bodega' importance is activity derived from confluent road and rail routes.

Away from these towns of the south-west, La Mancha has an empty landscape. Much of it is completely uninhabited, and the remainder sparsely scattered with large nucleated villages each with 5000 or 6000 inhabitants. Some of the smallest and poorest hamlets are made up entirely of cave dwellings excavated in the soft limestones: and even some of the larger centres, such as Villacañas with 9000 inhabitants, have large troglodyte sections. A density map would show a central area with less than 30 persons per square mile surrounded except on the east by a more densely populated belt. North of the Zancara-Guadiana, density rises to about 50, in the south-west to over 80, and even north-eastward towards Cuenca to over 40 per square mile.

Agriculturally dependent on variable yields of common wine and wheat, cursed by a killing climate without any soil makeweight, La Mancha is an area of poverty. Many of its inhabitants would consider themselves fortunate if even today they could eat as well as Cervantes' hero, who 'with minced meat on most nights, lentils on Fridays, and a pigeon extraordinary on Sundays, consumed three-quarters of his revenue'.

THE THRESHOLD REGION OF JÚCAR

Extending eastwards from La Mancha, a prolongation of the Tertiary basin of the southern Meseta thrusts between the Iberian mountains and the Betic Cordillera almost to the coastal lowlands of Valencia. This corridor depression between the Mediterranean littoral and New Castile is of less importance to communication than one would expect from an examination of a topographic map. Only one railway connects the 'huertas' with the interior, and that leads tortuously along the edge of the southern highlands via Almansa and Albacete. A second line has almost been completed which will for the first time link Valencia directly with Castile, routed via Utiel and Cuenca through the foothills of the Iberian ranges. It is noteworthy that road and rail alignments avoid the central valleys of the depression, and the main settlements hug the northern and southern hills.

This avoidance of the plateau-edge valleys, so characteristic of Spain, is a result of climatic and topographic factors. The extreme seasonal fluctuations in river flow make the valley lands liable to sudden and catastrophic floods. Cultivation is hazardous, and road and rail construction difficult and expensive. Since the rivers cut through the resistant plateau-edge rocks in narrow deep gorges, and the gradients of the eastward descent are very steep, the valleys do not provide lines of easy movement.

For these reasons the threshold region of the Júcar, although historically important as a corridor zone, has always been controlled from bases set back in the interior—Cuenca and Albacete. Settlement is sparse on the table-land, and confined to a few restricted sites in the valleys. In most respects human activity is similar to that of La Mancha.

THE SIERRAS OF GUADELUPE AND TOLEDO

Rising above the general level of the southern Meseta and extending from Trujillo to a point south of Toledo is a belt of broken highland. Formed of elevated basal granites, these sierras also have volcanic and Palaeozoic constituents. The general structural and topographical alignment is from west to east although ranges such as that of Sierra de Altamira diverge considerably.

The general highland level of 2300 ft. is only 500–600 ft. above that of New Castile, and the higher summits rarely attain much over 3000 ft. in the Montes de Toledo. Farther westward where the highland zone is narrowest individual peaks reach 4500 ft.

Narrow, discontinuous and of medium height these mountains nevertheless form a negative barrier belt between the Tagus and Guadiana lands. Too low to have much orographic effect on rainfall, or even to have anything more than showers of snow, and composed of resistant and acid siallitic rocks, this region presents considerable difficulties to exploitation and to crossing. Its naked summits are strewn with rugged quartzite boulders fragmented by frost action. The slopes, with thin acid soils, are covered by screes and 'matorral'. Only in a few depressions is settlement possible.

The region suffers also from the poverty of the surrounding areas. Communications are ill developed not only because of local topographic difficulty and ecological poverty, but also because the southern Meseta as a whole is sparsely populated. What traffic exists moves east–west along the main basins of the Tagus and Guadiana and north–south either along the Portuguese frontier or from New Castile to Despeñaperros. These Sierras are desolate and ignored to a much greater extent than any atlas map would suggest.

EXTRAMADURA

The western half of the southern Meseta is composed of basal old rocks akin to those of the Sierra Morena and the western

Cantabrians. This Palaeozoic platform has been elevated and faulted, and now survives as a slightly dissected 'senile' plateau tilted downwards to the west. Between Mérida and Badajoz the Primary rocks are down-thrown to form a small, isolated depression. This basin, partly tectonic in origin, is infilled with Tertiary and Recent sedimentary rocks that contrast markedly with the surrounding crystalline beds.

The climate of Extramadura is slightly affected by Atlantic influences, these rapidly dying out towards the east. Badajoz, for instance, experiences barometric changes quite different from those of La Mancha. At Ciudad Real and at Albacete pressure remains high from November to August, and the barometric drop in late summer is small. At Badajoz and Cáceres two maxima and minima occur, marking the half-yearly development of cyclonic instability. Summer temperatures remain high, averaging over 68° F. from June to September; and both the August mean of 81° F. and the recorded maximum of 117° F. are higher than for the interior. Winter temperatures are generally similar to those of Old Castile, and are considerably affected by altitude and exposure. The contrast between the high plateaux and the depressions is best brought out by the difference between the diurnal thermal ranges—19° F. at sheltered 600 ft. high Badajoz, and 24° F. on the 2110-ft.-high ridge of Cáceres.

The distinction between the climatic régimes of western Extramadura and New Castile is mainly one of humidity and precipitation. Winter relative humidity is much the same, 81 at Badajoz and 79 at Madrid, but in summer it remains much higher at the western station—Badajoz 59, Madrid 39. Annual rainfall averages are the same for the two stations but while Madrid has marked maxima in May and November, Badajoz has a single rainy period between October and May.

These climatic differences, slight though they may be, are of some ecological importance. On the crystalline parent rocks slow weathering has produced dry siallitic soils of low lime content. In some areas, as around Cáceres and on the tableland of La Serena, these degenerate into sands of very low fertility. South of Badajoz, on the Tierra de Barros, admixture of Tertiary calcareous material has produced good fertile loams.

Grasses do not generally flourish on these dry acid soils, but the slightly greater humidity allows scrub vegetation of brambles and evergreen oak to cover virtually all the broken land. Therefore although the table-lands are windswept and bare, the scattered rather shaggy hill-slopes make the landscape very different from the champaign country of La Mancha.

Agriculture, however, is at a disadvantage compared with that of the rest of the southern Meseta. Like the Salamanca region of Old Castile, Extramadura neither has plentiful rain nor chemically fertile dry soils. Uncultivated wasteland extends over about one-third of the area. With the exception of the Badajoz basin, most of the remainder of the region can only produce a crop once in every five or six years. The general system is of a year's bare fallow, a cereal crop, and then two or more years of reversion to rough grazing. The sudden onset in May of high temperatures and aridity make it necessary for wheats to be of very early varieties. Poor soil conditions encourage the cultivation of oats, which as a 'safe' crop are equal to wheat in importance in this region. Summer aridity and low winter temperatures make the olive more important than the vine except in the Badajoz area. Other crops are only grown with difficulty for local subsistence, again with the exception of the Guadiana Tertiary depiession, where small-scale irrigation and relatively sheltered calcareous soils combine to produce a small oasis of mixed agriculture.

Sheep raising, always important, has today made western Extramadura the chief wool-producing area of Spain. In the days of Mesta supremacy most of the region was held by the three great military orders as pastureland. Around Alcántara on the lower Tagus, on the Mérida lands of the Order of Santiago, and on the pastures of La Serena held by Calatrava, thousands of merino sheep found winter sustenance. The great Cañadas, Leonesa and Segoviana, led northward to the summer pastures of the Asturias and southern Navarre. This long-range transhumance has persisted to a certain extent to the present day, although movement other than by rail has become more localised.

The combination of long fallow cultivation and seasonal pasturing of sheep in an area of patchy scrub forest has produced one of the most complicated of the many complex Spanish systems of land use, known as 'Baldios'. Under this arrangement, up to four separate groups of users exploit the land. Sedentary pastoralists mainly interested in oak-mast for swine, seasonal sheep-herders, charcoal burners and catch-crop cultivators—each of these may hold different rights of usage. This is a measure of the pressure on limited resources. The low permanent carrying capacity of the land is also mainly responsible for the large size of most properties. In 1930, Badajoz and Cáceres provinces with almost 62% of their area in estates larger than 500 acres, were the classic regions of 'Latifundias'. Some of these large holdings have now been subdivided and more closely settled under the auspices of the Instituto Nacional de Colonización, but except in planned irrigation zones, the viability of small farms is doubtful.

As might be expected, population density is low, averaging about 60 per square mile in the region as a whole. The slightly higher density than that of New Castile is doubtfully explicable on environmental grounds, but is rather due to the absence of any urban or industrial attraction away from the land. Cáceres and Badajoz are the only towns with populations of over 25,000, and even they rank little higher than the scattered nucleated villages each with some 10,000 inhabitants.

The Tagus valley, narrow and of little importance as a routeway, is less closely settled than the piedmont area below the Central Sierras, where many small villages lie in relatively well-watered re-entrants. Puente de Arzobispo, an old crossing point, is one of the few centres on the Tagus. The slopes of the Montes de Toledo and the Guadiana basin downstream to Mérida are both thinly peopled, although the village clusters are slightly closer in the lower lands.

Cáceres, Badajoz and Mérida have all had one function in common, that of guarding and commanding a frontier region.

Physically and culturally western Extramadura and southern Portugal have much in common, and the political frontier is here less geographically defined than anywhere else on the borders of Spain. In Roman days Cáceres was a capital of Lusitania, the province of south-west Iberia, and Mérida (Emerita Augusta) was an important post on the main highway between Toledo (Toletum) and Lisbon. Cáceres is now the provincial capital of an agricultural area that can just support one town, while Mérida, a small market and rural centre, has lost the lead to Badajoz—its Roman rival. Badajoz grew most rapidly as the centre of a Moorish kingdom, and after Portuguese separatism proved too strong for Castile to break down became an obvious border strongpoint. Well served by the relatively fertile lands to the east, with a fortified hill-centre, its only advantage over Mérida lay in its nearness to the frontier. Besieged successfully and unsuccessfully on scores of occasions, it has now relapsed into provincial peace as a regional capital and economic centre.

Extramadura, aesthetically, has one of the least satisfying landscapes of Spain. Andalusia, lying no great distance over the easy northern slopes of the Sierra Morena, must have seemed a very Paradise to the Christian reconquerors who marched and fought through the whole length of northern Spain.

Chapter XIII

SOUTHERN SPAIN: ANDALUSIA

ANDALUSIA can best be considered as made up of several distinctive sub-regions. Best known of these, and often referred to as though it alone comprised Andalusia, is the V-shaped Guadalquivir lowland, which extends inland for 250 miles as a narrowing triangle. Immediately north of this lowland lies the Sierra Morena, in one sense definitely not a part of Andalusia, since, as we have already noted (Chapter II), it is merely a buckled and uptilted portion of the Meseta. But as a boundary zone, providing, so to speak, a northern frame to the lowlands, the Sierra Morena is in many respects best considered as a part of Andalusia, to which it is strongly linked by economic and human ties.

The southern side of the triangle is made up by the Betic Cordillera, which gradually approaches the Sierra Morena towards the east, forming an apex to the triangle, the third side of which is the Atlantic Ocean between Huelva and Cape Trafalgar.

THE GUADALQUIVIR LOWLANDS

Although on a large scale map this region appears a simple lowland, there is in reality a somewhat surprising variety in local topography and appearance of the countryside itself. This is because of the different rock strata which occur. In the extreme north-east (at the acute angle formed between the Betic Cordillera and Sierra Morena) rocks of Mesozoic age predominate (chiefly Triassic) with extensive beds of marl and gypsum. The marls are sometimes banded and brightly coloured, giving as it were a 'striped' effect to the landscape. Under the prevailing semi-arid conditions both rocks produce only a thin soil which, on gypsum particularly, can become very poor and even sterile, giving an open, monotonous landscape that in parts becomes really desolate. Bare expanses of thin soil or even bedrock itself alternate with a scanty covering of esparto-grass, tamarisk and thorn bush.

Gradually, however, as one moves westward, rocks of younger age replace the Triassic series. Cretaceous measures of chalk and loam occur on the southern bank of the Guadalquivir, and are distinctly more fertile, supporting intensive cereal farming. Farther west still, round Córdoba and Seville, there is a complex of Tertiary rock series. These were laid down in shallow seas which alternately spread inland and retreated as the result of slight oscillations of the land surface. In consequence, there is no one dominant rock measure, nor even a regular succession; but instead, zones of Tertiary strata laid down almost like a mosaic, marly limestones like those of the centre of the Paris basin, purer limestone, chalk, sands and clays. In the main, the countryside of the middle and lower Guadalquivir is extremely open and flat, but slight differences in resistance to erosion displayed by the various rock strata have produced small-scale ravines, isolated hillocks, and occasional low ridges with dips and scarps.

Another significant feature is that the Guadalquivir itself does not flow down the centre of its valley—it lies well to the north, much nearer the Sierra Morena; pushed as it were towards the northern side of the Andalusian plain, and far from symmetrically placed within its basin. Consequently, its northern tributaries are in general short and poorly developed, whilst its southern affluents, coming from the wetter Betic Cordillera, are more numerous and stronger, with a far greater volume of water.

The local differences in rock, and hence in soils, are of some importance, since they greatly influence the crops grown. On the heavier clayey soils cereals are extensively cultivated—wheat, maize, barley and oats, with few variations from this general pattern which amounts to monoculture. Closer to the river, where more varied soils occur (due both to erosion of the Tertiary rock beds and deposition by the river) rice growing by irrigation and the cultivation of olives are found; whilst in a few restricted zones (e.g. Jerez, Seville and Jaén) vines are the dominant crop. In a few places, soil salinity is a feature, and here occur semi-sterile basins that are much less productive than the rest of this region. The two [kinds of badland— gypsum exposures and salt basins—are, however, of relatively small extent: and the open cereal-clad lowlands (known as

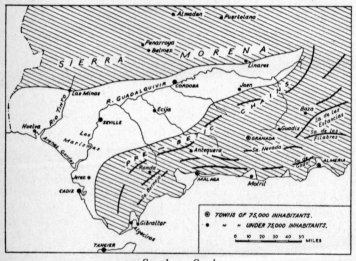

17 Southern Spain

campañas), together with the vines and olive-groves, make up a region that has had a reputation for agricultural richness since the first millennium B.C. Some districts have been in cultivation more or less continuously for 3000 years, and the high proportion of the Plain of Andalusia that is actually under cultivation is in marked contrast to the north, east and south, where wide areas of intermittently cultivated or unused lands are found.

Four 'huerta' or 'vega' areas occur—at Jaén, Córdoba and north and south of Ecija. Here, besides fruit and cereals, cotton, tobacco and sugar are intensively cultivated by the use of irrigation water—all but tobacco a legacy of Arab days.

The richness of the Plain is most apparent in the stretch

between Córdoba and Jaén, on the south side especially of the Guadalquivir. Here the amount of poor land is at a minimum, and the variety of crops is greatest. Sugar (beet and cane), oranges and many other fruit trees diversify the landscape; and the occurrence of palms and cactus-hedges is a reminder of the former importance of Seville and Cádiz as gateways to Africa and the New World.

In the stretch between Córdoba and Seville the same pattern of cultivation occurs, but there are more extensive areas of incompletely used or wholly uncultivated land. These often lie on the 'middle' river terraces, where water supply is difficult, or where sterile sands form the subsoil. Such zones are sometimes used as grazing for cattle or often bulls, the rearing of which is an important activity, since Andalusian bulls have a reputation for 'gameness' and ferocity in *corridas*.

Below Seville the plain becomes flatter, and the main features of relief are a line of large dunes, the Arenas Gordas, which run parallel to the coast. Behind this barrier the Guadalquivir spreads out in an expanse of tidal swamp—Las Marismas, with patches of higher ground, some of which are cultivated. At one period, probably within historic time, Las Marismas were one vast lake, which extended from the mouth of the river to within 10 miles of Seville. The intervening ridges of higher ground consist partly of fertile alluvium, partly of infertile sands—hence agricultural possibilities are restricted.

On the higher land away from the valley centre, sometimes on the scarps and higher river terraces, but more often along the actual foothills of the Sierra Murcia and Betic Cordillera, vine growing becomes the principal activity. By far the most important wine-producing region lies around Jerez de la Frontera, which gives its name to 'sherry'. As genuine port wines originate near Oporto, so real sherry can come only from the Jerez district. A cheaper kind of table wine resembling *vin ordinaire* is produced in larger quantity from the other vine-growing areas of Andalusia (Jaén, Córdoba and Seville), but in value, if not in amount, the sherry district is by far the most significant.

Sherry is a 'heavy' blended wine, fortified by the addition

of sugar and distilled spirit. There are several kinds of sherry, reflecting closely the slightly differing geographical conditions under which they are produced. *Manzanilla* comes from the coastal districts, and is said to have a slight salt 'tang' of the sea: the greater summer heat of the interior terraces produces an especially dry wine (*Montilla* or *Amontillado*): whilst the somewhat cooler districts are often used for the making of *Oloroso* sherries—distinctly sweeter, and darker in colour. Sherry of a particular kind is a blend of small quantities of wine from many different vineyards and differing districts, so that there is no such thing as a vintage sherry. The aim is to produce exactly the same end-product year by year, from individual wines that inevitably reflect the annual variation in local climate and treatment, and the slight differences in geographical terrain where vines are grown.

Climate. Compared with the adjacent Meseta or the Iberian mountains, the Andalusian plain enjoys extremely favourable climatic conditions. But this is to some extent only relative, as there are three pronounced disadvantages: excessive summer heat, especially inland; and scantiness and irregularity of rainfall. Winter conditions are on the whole very pleasant—the mean January temperature lies between 50° and 55° F.—being somewhat warmer on the coast; here frosts are very rare indeed, but inland slight frost can occur once or twice each winter. Day temperatures are quite high, averaging 60–65° F., with the highest day maxima occurring inland—an interesting example of the differential effects of solar heating as between land and sea.

In summer however (as noted in Chapter III), the Andalusian lowlands are the hottest part of Spain (and also Europe), with temperatures above 100° F. Wide diurnal range produces an evening coolness which mitigates the worst effects of the day; but, on the other hand, the plain is subject to a hot dry easterly current, the *solano*, which is further dried out and warmed by a descent from the ring of hills to the east. This in summer produces torrid suffocating weather which adversely affects plant, animal and human life.

Rainfall is heaviest on the coast, where it averages 20-25 ins.,
a gradual decrease occurs inland, 10-15 ins. being the mean.
From June to September hardly any rain falls. March is usually the wettest month, but there are pronounced fluctuations
from year to year. As little as 5 ins. or as much as 36 ins. have
fallen in one year; and over 6 ins. in one day. Thus, drought
can alternate with floods, and one region experience the one
whilst its near neighbour is affected by the other.

The climatic differences as between the coastal zone and the
interior may at first appear slight, but they are of considerable
significance in the distribution of plants. Within the lower
valley, the date and orange flourish: east of Seville, they do
not.

Towns. Predominance in lowland Andalusia is disputed between Seville and Cádiz. The former, at the head of tidewater
on the Guadalquivir, and the lowest bridging-point, is the
natural market and administrative centre for the richest part
of the valley, and is by far the larger (450,000 inhabitants).
Besides its exchange function, it has developed local industries
based on the transformation of local products—oil pressing,
wine and tobacco making, pottery and light manufactures, and
textiles based on silk and wool. In the 15th century Seville had
a considerable silk industry, said to have employed 100,000
workers; and it was also the leading commercial centre of
southern Spain.

At this time Seville held a legal monopoly of sea-traffic with
the south and west; but when this monopoly was broken by
Cádiz (after centuries of effort) the importance of Seville declined. The goods manufactured in Seville, once sold throughout much of Spain and its colonies, could in the end no longer
compete with other European wares imported through Cádiz
and re-exported to the Americas. Hence since the 16th century Seville has lost much of its former importance.

Cádiz, better placed for ocean trading, has become an important gateway into southern and central Spain, and is now
again increasing in size after a period of decline. Present population is 123,000; and besides its functions as a port, subsidiary

industries have grown up—food processing and manufacturing. With recent United States interest in Spain (which, incidentally, is producing considerable changes in outlook throughout Spain), Cádiz has profited from the greater volume of traffic between the two countries. Its position on a narrow peninsula, and at the seaward end of the only large and easily negotiable lowland corridor that gives access to central Spain, is the main factor in its present day growth.

The feature of local market with a few associated small-scale industries is common in Andalusia. Córdoba (207,000) ranks as the third town of Andalusia; and in Moslem days had a considerable reputation as a manufacturing and intellectual centre. But with the fall in population since mediaeval times its activities have declined, and the fact that it does not lie on a major routeway is a handicap. The main route from Madrid to the extreme south passes well to the east, by the Pass of Despeñaperros (= Downfall of the Dogs—a reference to a defeat of the Moslems). Jaén (70,000) is another market town lying in the most fertile part of a rather dry and difficult district—the occurrence of porous limestone series in the surrounding areas being a handicap.

THE SIERRA MORENA

The Sierra is by no means a single line of hills, but rather a complex of minor ridges aligned from east-north-east to south-south-west, with the highest points just over 3500 ft. in height. As compared with many of the mountain massifs in Spain, the Sierra Morena has few outstanding peaks or even massive plateaux, though on its southern side, where it overhangs the Guadalquivir lowlands, it appears imposing enough. To the geologist the Sierra offers a number of interesting problems—particularly as to its period and mode of origin, and the extent to which the structures can be regarded as true folds. For the geographer, main interest lies in its southern, abrupt face, which sharply delimits the Plain of Andalusia; and the extent and variety of mineral deposits. Because of the geological age of the rocks composing the Sierra Morena, some writers draw an analogy with Hercynian Europe—especially central Germany, which shows a similar broken topography with a high degree of mineralisation.

Copper is the most abundant metal, and is located chiefly in the western parts of the Sierra (Huelva, Rio Tinto). The mineral is associated with igneous dykes, and occurs mainly as pyrites (in fact, forming the most extensive pyrites deposits of the whole world). Iron and sulphur are also found close to the copper in the same igneous formations.

Lead and silver occur in the centre and east of the Sierra (at Belmez, Linares and Peñarroyo); and at Almadén there are the famous mercury mines that have been exploited at least since the first millennium B.C. Almost every mediaeval glass mirror made in Europe used Almadén mercury, and monopolist control of this metal was the mainstay of the wealth of the Fuggers of Augsburg, who gave essential financial support to the Holy Roman Emperors.

A further favourable circumstance is the occurrence in the Sierra of beds of coal, preserved in downfolds at Puertollano and Penarroyo. With a total annual output of about one million tons, these coal measures facilitate concentration of the mineral ores produced nearby. It is, however, significant of the relatively low level of industrial activity in Spain that the concentrates are usually sent abroad for smelting and refining.

Despite the advantages outlined above, the exploitation of minerals has not led to the growth of an industrial region in the Sierra Morena. Most producing areas remain primitive, like New World mining camps, with the ores only partially treated and then moved elsewhere. Many of the concessions were, and still are, foreign owned (e.g. those at Penarroyo are mainly French, and at Rio Tinto British); and with copper, at least, it would seem that following twenty centuries of exploitation the peak of production has been passed, since the ore-body is becoming less rich the deeper it is mined. Consequently, output has declined during the last half-century. A further difficulty is the absence of an industrial artisan population within the region. However, the present Spanish government has announced a programme of mineral prospection, to try to discover more deep-seated lodes, together with the establish-ment of small scale industries in the nearby villages, using metals as raw material. Other than in the mining areas the Sierra re-mains a relatively empty territory, broken by ravines, and covered in its higher parts by scrub vegetation. In a few dis-tricts, arable farming is carried on, but over most of the up-lands pastoralism is the main occupation.

THE BETIC CORDILLERA

Including the associated lowlands, lying between the up-land ridges and along the Mediterranean coast, the Betic Cordillera is approximately equal in area to the Guadalquivir plain and covers eight modern provinces. In structure, the Cordillera is best regarded as two separate and unequal chains separated by a central region of lower relief. The northern chain is composed of folded sedimentary rocks, chiefly Meso-zoic limestones; and the southerly one is made up of nappe-structures (with one rock layer impacted against another) so that much metamorphism has taken place, with extensive de-velopment of gneiss and schists. Granites are also to be found. Where the nappes meet the younger sedimentary strata, a line of weakness occurs, and this has produced the intermediate lower zone, referred to above, which runs in the main from east to west. The whole Cordillera is arranged roughly in the shape of a pot-hook lying on its side.

Although both chains are of considerable height, they are also narrow, so that rivers running north or south on their flanks have cut back deep valleys, which in certain instances extend completely through the mountain ridges, dividing them into sections. The entire Cordillera is hence split into small component upland massifs, the major line of division being the longitudinal east–west running valley, the minor lines being north–south running passes.

The Sub-Betic Chain. There are marked differences between the northern chain (known as the sub-Betic or pre-Betic uplands), and the southern, or main Betic Cordillera. The former, being composed of less resistant sedimentaries, and also lying some-what farther away from the centre of tectonic disturbance, is of distinctly lower height. Fewer parts exceed 6000 ft. in altitude; whereas the main Cordillera, being harder and more subjected to earth-movements, rises to over 11,000 ft. in its highest section, the Sierra Nevada, and many parts are over 10,000 ft.

Moreover, the main Cordillera is composed of impermeable rocks, so that more of the actual precipitation remains at the surface for effective use by man. The sub-Betic ridges, on the other hand, are made up of porous limestones, so that they are distinctly drier, both because, being lower, there is less oro-graphic rain, and also such precipitation as occurs tends to percolate underground. As a result, the sub-Betic zone is markedly less attractive for settlement; and there is the some-what unusual situation that the higher and more rugged up-land is in general more densely populated than the lower and more accessible pre-Betic zone.

In fact, much of the pre-Betic area is a classic 'karst' region where erosion effects upon massive Jurassic and Cretaceous limestones are well developed. One such area, a 'text-book' instance, in its extreme karst development is that of Antequera, in the central part of the range; and another lies in the east, where the sub-Betic chain joins the Sierra Morena. In both districts conditions are extremely forbidding. Settlement is almost entirely absent, and through routes from north to south tend to avoid these areas.

The upper slopes of the ridges generally are bare of trees —sometimes even of soil. But at lower levels, where red clay characteristic of limestone areas has been deposited, there are patches of forest, or of cultivation. It is too cold (owing to alti-tude) for the olive, but there is some cereal growing, with pas-turing of sheep and goats on the higher slopes where scanty vegetation occurs. The west is on the whole distinctly more favoured than the east. Lying nearer the Atlantic, it receives a substantially heavier annual rainfall, and since altitude is lower, the cold of winter is less pronounced.

General difficulty of conditions, with really harsh natural limitations, have made the sub-Betic zone one of considerable isolation and scattered settlement. Many villages are placed high on rocky spurs or crop, away from the valley-floors, and are approachable only by terrifying paths, or at best, tortuous and ill-made roads. Despite the presence of certain main through routes from central and eastern Spain, the inhabitants have tended to live apart from the rest of Andalusia, and remoteness and difficulty of access are highly characteristic. For centuries the zone was a 'buffer' or 'no man's land' between Christian and Moslem Spain. The addition of *de la Frontera* to many place-names of this part of Andalusia indicates its special situation as a marchland.

THE BETIC AREA

This consists of massive ridges aligned from west to east, but again with a deflection southwards in the west, and northwards in the east. Here occur the highest summits in Spain: Mulhacén (11,420 ft.) and Veleta (11,246 ft.). Below these peaks are extensive eroded areas, showing much glacial action (cirques and moraines) at levels lower than those reached by permanent snow, which is now limited to the northern aspects of the two high peaks. In one sense, then, the Sierra Nevada only just manages to deserve its name—but snow lies for eight to eleven months on a much more extensive area—and it can snow even in July and August at heights above 10,000 ft.

The Sierra Nevada proper (as has already been mentioned in Chapter II) only extends for about 45 miles south-east of Granada. The remaining ridges of the main Betic Cordillera are: to the east, the Sierra de los Estancias and Sa. de los Filabres; to the south, Sa. Contravesia and Sa. de Gador; and to the west the Sa. Tejeda, Sa. de la Nieve and Sa. Bermeja. All of these average only 6000 ft. at most in height, but the differences of component rock type—white (limestone), dark grey (gneiss), red and green (granites), adds variety to their landscape. In the extreme south these ridges sweep down to the Mediterranean sometimes with a small intervening coastal plain, where there is sufficient level land and alluvial soil for a 'huerta' and urban settlement. In many instances, however, the mountain ridges reach the sea directly in a series of cliffs.

Some, but not all, of the uplands are forested, and on the Sierra Nevada there is a clear vegetation succession. Mediterranean plants extend from sea level to 3000–4000 ft. (depending on aspect), then heathland of broom and thorns (formerly coniferous woodland), above 5000 ft. temperate grassland, which ultimately changes first to Alpine meadowland, and finally Alpine tundra.

Occasional patches of the higher ground are cultivated: in wheat, barley and maize to 6500 ft., then with potatoes and rye another 1500–2000 ft. higher still. The higher mountain slopes lend themselves particularly well to local but well-developed transhumance, exactly like that of the Alps and Pyrenees. Animals and their herds move upwards from the valleys as the snow melts, ultimately spending a few weeks at heights of 8000–10,000 ft. for a few weeks during the height of summer.

The whole area, with its steep slopes broken by deep ravines, remained until very recently in considerable physical and human isolation. Ways of life altered only slowly, with blood feuds, vendettas and patriarchal dominance common features of existence. It is significant that the inhabitants of the higher Cordilleras did not fully recognise the rule of the Arabs whose capital was only a few miles away. After the fall of Moslem Granada in 1492, resistance to the Christians continued in these parts for another eighty years—an interesting example of geographical inertia. In the end, many of the inhabitants were exterminated and the district re-settled by immigrants from Galicia.

One incompletely used resource of the Betic Cordillera is its minerals. Iron, lead and zinc have been exploited sporadically throughout many of the Sierras over several centuries, and alluvial platinum is known to occur. More might be done to develop these deposits, but knowledge of the detailed geology is incomplete.

Between the various Sierras that comprise the Betic Cordillera lie areas of somewhat lower relief—not true lowlands, as some are over 2500 ft. in height—but definitely lower than the ridges and fairly level. Component rock-type varies a great deal, from fairly soft Mesozoic and Tertiary sediments to resistant and more ancient metamorphosed series. At the zones of contact of the porous sediments and impermeable schists and granites there are often copious springs, with patches of fertile alluvial soil. Here intensive cultivation can be carried on.

The largest of these high-level basins is that round Granada. Others are at Guadix–Baza, Alpujarras, Angequera–Campillas and Ronda, with the westernmost (and lowest) running inland from the coast at Gibraltar–Algeciras. In those basins that lie at over 2000 ft., winters are distinctly cold and the range of crops produced is reduced. Elsewhere, despite a distinctly low January mean temperature, there can occur small zones where abundant water, favourable climate and a rich soil (derived from erosion of many differing rock series) allow a level of cultivation that was a byword for richness. Many observers have noted a similarity to conditions in south-west Asia or North Africa—these basins of the Betic Cordillera much resemble oases such as Damascus, Tashkent, Konia, Isfahan or Cyrene. Cool rushing streams emerge from the base of barren, eroded hills, and are led off by a multitude of ingenious small canals to garden plots growing a great variety of exotic crops.

By no means all basins, however, are fertile. Exposure of marl or gypsum can give rise (as on the lowlands of Andalusia) to considerable soil salinity. Sterile 'badlands' are therefore a feature, being particularly developed in the centre and east, in the regions of Guadix, Baza and Campillas. One remarkable characteristic in the districts of sterile or overcharged soils is the practice by the inhabitants of living in caves, as in La Mancha. Troglodyte communities are fairly common, thus adding to the desolate appearance of the landscape, which lacks villages.

The largest town of the Betic region is Granada (158,000). Once it was the market-garden and economic mainstay of the Arab Kingdom of Córdoba, and the Alhambra (the royal palace) is regarded by many as the finest achievement of Arab architecture in any country. A faint reflection of the former splendour and opulence of the city remains to colour the imagination of cinema owners in Britain and elsewhere. Nowadays, its function is more modest. Beyond limited tourist attractions, a nodal position on one or two major north–south gaps through the Cordillera—though this was not until recently followed by a railway—its function is merely that of a large regional market town. Guadix lies on one of the two railway lines that penetrate the Cordillera to reach Almeria and Málaga: Granada has no direct rail link with the south. Instead, the main line of railway communication was from east to west from Murcia towards Málaga, Algeciras and Seville, using the series of depressions lying between the main Cordillera and the sub-Betic ranges.

The remaining district is that of the south coast. Here too is an alternation of amazingly fertile 'huerta' and barren rocky spurs which penetrate to the Mediterranean and isolate one coastal lowland from another. The largest and most fertile of these enclaves is that surrounding Málaga; with others at Velez Málaga, Almeria and Motril.

Frost is unknown on these coastlands, and although rainfall is scanty (7–12 ins. only), abundant supplies of irrigation water from the interior can make up the difference, provided that man is active and intelligent enough to construct the necessary canals. Agriculture here has a distinctive aspect. Cotton, dates, sugar-cane and sweet potatoes indicate the relative warmth of the winter season—this is a sub-tropical régime. Fruit, early vegetables and grapes are grown for export, and wine is made at Málaga and Velez Málaga. A speciality is the dried grapes known as muscatels; whilst Almeria specialises in fresh grapes for the table.

Besides agriculture there is a thriving fishing trade; and both Málaga (307,000) and Almeria (73,500) also export mineral ores produced from their hinterlands in the Betic Cordillera. Almeria has nearby deposits of iron, lead and copper, whilst Málaga has extensive iron-ore beds. Moreover, the picturesqueness of the topography, favourable climate, and easy accessibility attract a certain number of tourists, often from cruising ships.

In contrast to much of the interior of Andalusia (including the Guadalquivir lowlands), the Mediterranean coastlands of Andalusia are in active development, in spite of an already long tradition. New markets for exports of agricultural produce, some interest in mineral exploitation, a useful but as yet limited tourist industry, and a growing importance as ports of entry for the interior of Spain give an air of activity and purposeness to the region, which is often lacking elsewhere in the south. The great days of Seville, Córdoba and Granada have already been lived—these were in the times of the Arabs, and during the great age of Spanish expansion into the New World. To the outside visitor much of Andalusia is outstandingly picturesque and typically 'Spanish', but to a large degree increasingly distanced by more progressive regions elsewhere in the peninsula.

One indication of this is in the system of landholding. Andalusia, and especially the western half of the Guadalquivir lowland, is notoriously the territory of *latifundia*—'extensive' exploitation by absentee landlords, who retain considerable privileges and vast wealth. One such nobleman could in 1950 spend £200,000 sterling on the reception of guests at his daughter's wedding. Social historians see in the existence of *latifundia* (wealthy owners and landless peasant labourers) a continuation of the mediaeval Arab situation of a cultivating slave population ruled by Moslem nobles. At the Reconquest, it was easiest to replace the few Arab landlords by northern Spanish aristocrats, who had little bond between themselves and the servile tenant populations they were called on to rule. This situation, despite the efforts of Spanish kings since 1500, still remains; and it is thought that *latifundia* has increased rather than declined over the last hundred years.

Latifundia is not universal. In eastern Andalusia empty areas were colonised by peasants from northern Spain, and also from Germany. In these districts peasant ownership is the rule—consequently as regards tenancy there is an interesting contrast, with Andalusia reflecting different historical evolution between the cultivated lowlands and the empty frontier lands of the 15th–16th centuries.

Chapter 14

SOUTH-EASTERN SPAIN:
THE LEVANT

THE district lying between Cabo de Gata (just east of Almeria) and the lower Ebro delta hardly seems at first examination to deserve recognition as a separate region. But several features serve to distinguish it from the Andalusian coast to the west, and Catalonia to the north-east. In the first place, the trend of relief is markedly different. Both the regions just mentioned have upland ridges running parallel to the coastline, with longitudinal valleys or lines of depressions at some distance inland. In the Levant coastlands, however, mountain ridges run in many parts almost at right-angles to the coast, producing a much simpler river pattern. Rivers have a fairly straight and direct course as consequent streams (i.e. draining direct from high ground to sea level), instead of the intricate gridiron or trellis patterns of the Betic Cordillera and lower Ebro. Here, even large rivers have to weave an irregular way from one lowland area to another, since they are blocked from taking a course direct to the sea by the longitudinal ridges. The main rivers of the Levant (from north to south the Guadalaviar or Turia), Cabriel, Júcar, and Segura all have a 'consequent' line of flow in their middle and lower sections.

Moreover, the areas of actual lowland are more extensive. Hills reach the sea only in a few districts—at Capes de Gata and de la Nao, where prolongations of the Betic Cordillera occur, and also just south of the Ebro delta. Between these outlying spurs are extensive flat stretches, wide enough to develop marshes and lagoons.

Further, and probably more important, the Levant coastlands are the most specifically 'Mediterranean' areas of Spain as regards climate. Andalusia shows a little of maritime Atlantic and steppe influences, with the presence of high mountains imposing further local modifications: but in Murcia and Valencia, the two provinces comprising the Levant area, climatic influences are purely Mediterranean in character. Though the coasts of Africa lie farther away than at Málaga and Almeria, conditions come nearer in certain aspects of those of Algiers and Sicily. One is conscious of being fully within the Mediterranean basin.

The tongue of higher ground reaching the coast at Cape de la Nao serves as a minor division within the Levant area. To the south is the province of Murcia, with a narrower coastal plain, lower rainfall, and more saline, hence less fertile soils. To the north is Valencia, more open to the sea, with a wider plain, better watered, and more fertile. With these two provinces are also to be grouped the Balearic Islands.

MURCIA

This province can be described topographically as a relatively gradual transition from low coastal plain first to upland plateau and finally to high mountain in the interior. Instead of the sudden drop from bold ridges parallel to the coast with only small enclaves of lowland, there is a fairly well developed coastal plain fronting the Mediterranean, which is backed by a more extensive piedmont zone. The lowland has been built up out of the sea by the deposition of alluvium—one effect due to the 'grain' of the region being at right-angles to the set of the coast and sea-currents. The promontories formed of more resistant rock tend to gather alluvial deposits on their flanks, consequently Murcia has a coastline of emergence: with lagoons, sea-marshes, spits and broad sandy bays.

One effect of the more gradual but prolonged descent from interior highland to coastal lowland is strongly shown in the climate of Murcia. The westerly air-streams, on descending from the plateau, gain heat through pressure change, and so give little rain. The south-easterlies blow from North

Africa, and have insufficient sea track to acquire much moisture. Aridity is therefore the chief climatic feature of Murcia, which lies in a pronounced 'rain shadow' relative to the Meseta. Skies are particularly clear—Murcia is spoken of in Spain as 'the serene province' and at one spot in the extreme south annual rainfall totals only 4½ ins., the lowest in Europe.

The effects of warm drying winds are also intensified by the nature of the rock, much of which, away from the coastal plain, consists of Cretaceous limestone or Tertiary marl. Intensive evaporation, acting on a surface already highly charged with minerals, produces soil salinity—the *salares*, more developed in Murcia than in any other part of Spain. At the same time, the semi-desert conditions in coastal Murcia encourage an unusual flora. The date palm is thoroughly at home (one of the very few areas in Europe of which this can be said). At Elche cultivated palms reach 70 or 100 ft. in height.

Another drawback in Murcia besides aridity is rainfall unreliability, which is here probably at its maximum for Spain. Droughts may be succeeded by floods; the river Segura (on which Murcia city stands) has a particularly bad reputation for disastrous overflow which can destroy villages and reservoirs and cause extensive loss of life. Nevertheless, the Segura has many barrages both for irrigation and for hydro-electric power.

Much of Murcia is steppe or semi-desert, with a very poor, thin esparto grass steppe as the characteristic vegetation. Cultivation is closely confined to the neighbourhood of streams, or where irrigation water is available, as in the 'huertas' of Murcia, Lorca, Elche and Alicante. Rainfall is by itself insufficient for agriculture.

Inland, the hill slopes show many signs of the destruction of what were once extensive forests of Mediterranean pine and cork-oak—a contributory factor to the flooding of the lowlands. Owing to surrounding barrenness, the irrigated areas appear as veritable oases (even to the palm trees), and here there is the usual extensive and luxurious range of crops. Fruit, vegetables, vines and olives, together with hemp and mulberry trees (both the basis of local manufacturing industries) are produced, together with lucerne, the growing of which (as fodder) is essential for animal rearing, since natural pasture is lacking.

Mineral deposits provide an important economic asset. Iron, lead and silver occur, chiefly in the Sierra de Almenara,

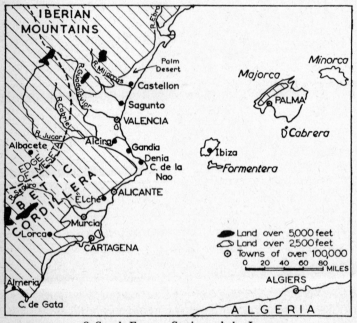

18 South-Eastern Spain and the Levant

west of Cartagena. This town of Carthaginian origin (as the name denotes) has something of a modern industry, using imported fuel and local ores; and its excellent harbour has made it a principal naval base. With its twin town, La Union, it also acts as a commercial port for the south-west of Spain, and is the principal outlet for Murcia city which also has a rail connection to Alicante, Cartagena's rival.

Murcia city (258,000) has the largest 'huerta' of the province, developed by elaborate canalisation of the waters of the Segura river and its tributary the Sangonera. Like many other towns of southern Spain, its main activities, beyond the functions of an administrative and market centre, are concerned with processing the products of its garden plots. The remaining large town, Alicante, is somewhat limited by the smaller size of its 'huerta' land, due to lack of irrigation water. It too is a port and produces a high-quality wine which is its chief export.

Despite the variety of occupations mentioned, Murcia appears as one of the areas of Mediterranean Spain that are less attractive to human settlement. The poverty of local resources in the interior is shown by the persistence of troglodyte communities and by a sustained stream of emigrants. Away from the ports and 'huerta' districts, which maintain and even increase their population, there is a marked drift away from the land, with rural depopulation. Migrants find their way to other countries of Europe (especially France) and to the Americas.

VALENCIA

Though the actual extent of lowland is hardly any greater than in Murcia, Valencia is an easier and richer land. There is the same pattern of a crescent-shaped coastal plain backed by hill country that sweeps to the sea into massive spurs, but, generally speaking, slopes are gentler (at least in the centre), and the countryside more open. A most significant point which further distinguishes Valencia from Murcia is that in the former, rivers are more developed, as the result of cutting back through the rim of the Meseta, and have captured some of the true Meseta streams. The Júcar, for instance, rises on the south-western slopes of the Montes Universales, then flows in a great semicircle southwards through Cuenca, ultimately turning east to reach the sea south of Valencia city. Its largest tributary, the Cabriel, is almost equally developed in its upper portion. Altogether, the Júcar is more than twice as long as the biggest river of Murcia, and this means greater possibilities for irrigation. Moreover, a higher volume of water has given rise to more developed river terracing, where 'huerta' agriculture can be carried on.

Consequently, in spite of similarities in climate and rock character (the predominant beds being limestone), Valencia, because of a more favourable topography and drainage pattern, offers greater human opportunities and is one of the most heavily populated provinces of Spain.

The extreme north-east of Valencia, the district of Maestrazgo, is a frontier area, marking the effective limits of southern Spain. Hill ranges, which attain 4000–6000 ft., come close to the sea, in the small Montes de Irta and Montes Atalayas. These form a topographical divide between the Valencian plain and the basin of the lower Ebro. The Maestrazgo is broken, and of an extreme karstic nature, so that settlement is sparse. One part, actually on the coast, is spoken of locally as the 'Palm tree Desert'.

There, farther south, comes the first of the larger streams, the Mijarras. Relief becomes more regular and open. Southwards still, we reach the main rivers, Palencia, Magro, Guadalaviar (or Turia), Júcar (with its tributary the Cabriel) and Serpis. The lowland is now much wider; and once again, as the result of extensive deposition of silt, there is a coastline of emergence, with coastal dunes, lagoons and salt marsh.

Along most of the coast, the dunes occur as fairly prominent features, often covered by stands of conifers. Behind them are the lagoons, the largest of which is the Albufera, south of Valencia city, with another of smaller size at Valencia itself. The lagoons support a certain amount of fishing, added to which is some hunting of the birds and wild creatures that inhabit the edges of the salt-marsh. This has produced a distinct community that lives not by agriculture, but from the fauna in and above the water, and with distinctive primitive dwellings—the *barracas*—osier-roofed huts with mud walls.

A few miles inland and extending north and south of Valencia is a zone of continuous cultivation some 50 miles long, and using the abundant river water for 'huerta' irrigation. The predominantly black soils of the district, strongly contrasting in colour with the Terra Rossa found elsewhere, are outstandingly fertile. Derived from varied and in the main easily eroded rock strata, their quality is further enriched by the alluvium brought down by the rivers.

The 'huertas' of Valencia have attracted the especial admiration and interest of visitors because of their intricate pattern of canals, and the highly intelligent use of water in relation to soil resources. This depends on enlightened democratic co-operation between the users, who have an elected Water Committee that has functioned for just about one thousand years. In some parts, two crops are taken each year and there is a most elaborate rotation of cereals, fruit, vegetables and other commercial plants such as tobacco, sugar and cotton. At lower levels, nearest the lagoons, rice is grown—Albufera being particularly well known for this.

Some regional differentiation is apparent, even within such a restricted area. In the north, where the encircling hills obtrude, vines and olives tend to predominate, with carobs on the lower ground. At Castellón emphasis is on citrus and other fruit trees; whilst vines, olives and fruit trees are also dominant in the south, round Alcira and Denia. Tomatoes and peppers are associated with the Gandia area.

Climatic conditions are the most favourable of Mediterranean Spain. Summers are distinctly cooler than those of Andalusia—7–9° F. cooler on average, whilst winters are almost as mild, and warmer than those of the neighbouring Ebro valley. Rainfall is by no means abundant, but is rather more spread throughout the year: no month is entirely rainless. This is not the case in the Guadalquivir valley. Also, fluctuations in onset of rain are somewhat less violent than in Murcia —though floods are by no means unknown. In Valencia one experiences most of the advantages of a true Mediterranean climate without certain of the extremes occurring elsewhere in southern Spain.

The continental shelf is at its widest off the coast of Valencia. Nowhere else in Spain does the 100-fathom line recede so far from the coast. This is partly responsible for the prevalence of shoals of tuna and other fish, which provide a livelihood for an important community living along the coast. The coast itself, being straight and shallow, does not offer outstandingly good harbour sites, but a number of small ports—Denia, Gandia, Villanueva del Grau (the outport of Valencia city) and Oropesa—have both a fishing trade and a small export activity in fruit (fresh and dried), wine and early vegetables.

A zonation of population tends to occur. Along the coast are scattered communities of fishermen, hunters, woodsmen and the merchants of the ports—some of which, it should be noted, are not precisely located on the coastline, but on a river a few miles inland. Then, in the area of lagoons and salt marsh, the population density is low. Some 5–10 miles inland lies the main 'huerta' zone, and here occur the extremely high concentration of farming populations that distinguishes the Valencian 'huertas'—2000–4000 persons per square mile. Valencia city, with a population of 571,000, ranks as the third town in Spain, after Madrid and Barcelona, a somewhat surprising situation in view of the predominantly agricultural character of the region. The 'huerta' of Valencia, which extends for 11 miles, has a further population of 400,000.

Valencia is obviously the dominating centre of the province, though it does not lie on the largest river (the Júcar); and its own river (the Guadalaviar) does not offer a practicable routeway westwards into the Meseta. Modern roads and the railway must swing either northwards to Sagunto and the Palencia valley, or southwards via the Martes and Upper Cabriel valley. The reason for Valencia's importance is the size and productivity of its 'huerta', which is the largest single expanse of fertile alluvium in Mediterranean Spain. The city is centrally placed in the lowland plain, and, like so many provincial capitals, acts as an exchange and administrative centre, with an assortment of local, small-scale industries.

Silk-making has some importance—once far more significant (as the imposing building of the Silk Guild indicates), together with other textiles (in wool and cotton), pottery, processing of fruit and vegetables, making of perfume and a flower trade. One very important seasonal activity is the export of oranges during winter. As they have a distinctive flavour not found in the Jaffa variety, there is a special trade, chiefly with northern Europe.

Valencia province has a long established tradition of town life. In contrast to Murcia, where there are large towns, scattered rural settlement and few villages, Valencia has a more consistent gradation from hamlet to city, with more of the larger rural settlements. Many, as for example Castellon, have maintained a number of basic activities over many centuries, with broadly the same way of life. Others, like Sagunto, have the same long-standing traditions as an urban centre with the accretion of modern activities—in this case, iron working on an important scale.

THE BALEARIC ISLANDS

The Balearic archipelago consists of four larger islands and seven very small, arranged in three groups. From west to east there are the Pityouses (Pine-islands) of Ibiza and Formentera; Majorca (Mallorca) by far the largest, with a neighbour, Cabrera; and Minorca (Menorca).

The islands represent a broken continuation of the Betic Cordillera: two ridges are discernible in Majorca, separated by a central plain, and one single ridge in Ibiza and Minorca. This is a simplification of a very complex pattern. It would be incorrect to regard the island group as merely one or two drowned fold-structures, since between the Pityouses and Majorca is a submarine trough, in parts over 3000 ft. deep. Within the islands themselves occurs considerable variation in topography and rock type. We are accustomed to seeing the Balearics on the map only as tiny appendages of Iberia; but with a total area of just under 2000 square miles the group is as large as a big English county, and Majorca alone is ten times the size of the Isle of Man.

Ibiza has an involved pattern of asymmetrical folds, involving beds of Triassic, Jurassic and Cretaceous age. The folds appear to have originated from the south-east, pushing, so to speak, the maximum disturbance (and hence highest ground) towards the north-west of the island. Formentera, on the other hand, is composed mainly of Tertiary and Quaternary rocks. Majorca has two distinct north-east–south-west running ridges which define the east and west coasts of the island, and are separated by a broad central plain. These ridges show the effects of intense folding, with the highest point, Puig Major, reaching 5100 ft. Altogether the shattered but still very imposing remains of the folds produce extremely striking scenery. The higher parts have a characteristic serrated appearance, giving a wild, bold skyline; while the lower parts near sea level appear as high cliffs enclosing sandy coves. Minorca shows a sharply opposed mixture of resistant Palaeozoic series (in the south-west, which is therefore hilly) and softer Tertiary strata in the north-east.

Climatically, the Balearics are of course clearly of the Mediterranean; but they show also special effects due to insular character. Ibiza, owing to proximity to the Spanish mainland, experiences the desiccating southerly winds (*calinas*) which dry up the coastlands of Murcia and Andalusia. Minorca, standing farthest into the Mediterranean, is the wettest of the islands; and the interior of Majorca, thanks to its coastal ridges, tends to be sheltered from the colder northern winds of winter. A special feature of the Balearics is the greater extent of dewfall than is common in most of Spain.

Temperatures are slightly lower in summer, and a little higher in winter; whilst rainfall averages 16–25 ins. annually, the driest district being that of the central lowland of Majorca —Ibiza is, however, the driest island as a whole. A pronounced autumnal maximum of rainfall indicates affinities to the nearby coasts of Spain and France. The summers are not entirely without rainfall, and their aridity is mitigated by the especially copious dews of the early summer months. These dews considerably affect the natural vegetation, which in Majorca especially strikes the visitor as particularly profuse and luxuriant.

In vegetation, as in climate, the islands reflect their geographical location as a stepping-stone to Italy. It has been remarked that the climate has certain Italian characteristics; and a proportion of the flora closely resembles that of Sardinia,

Corsica, Sicily and Crete. Certain species indigenous to the Spanish mainland are moreover absent—in other words, the Balearics are a frontier zone between two botanical provinces.

Within the islands occur limited opportunities for agriculture and fishing. The central plain of Majorca, with its deeper soils, offers the best return—the limiting factor is rainfall. Cereals, early vegetables and fruit crops (especially potatoes and oranges) are grown, but the predominating tree is the almond, which at times, depending on the state of the international market, covers nearly a half of the cultivated surface of Majorca. Elsewhere, the countryside can pass into rugged ravines or karstic conditions, so that here animal herding is the only occupation.

Fishing is less important than would seem reasonable in an island cluster. A considerable drawback is the unevenness of the sea-floor which, as we have noted, has ridges and major 'deeps' that inhibit trawling. Of recent years, tourism has become a principal activity, especially in Majorca. Accessibility by sea and air (more particularly from the north and west), the warm and dry but not overwhelmingly hot summers and remarkably picturesque scenery are all favourable factors, and with 'tourist' rates for air travel, the clientèle is no longer limited to the wealthy or eccentric from central Europe; the Co-operative Traveller from Britain has tended to replace Chopin and George Sand.

In addition, however, the Balearics have a special geographical location at the crossing of major routeways—one from eastern Spain to Italy and Sicily (we may recall that Italy has been ruled from Spain, and that the Kingdom of Aragon once included Sicily and Malta) and the other from Mediterranean France to North Africa and the Atlantic. The Balearics have thus been within the main streams of western Mediterranean activity, in marked contrast to nearby islands such as Corsica and Sardinia. Outside influence and contacts have developed in a way denied to other regions. Natives of the islands have taken part in overseas trading, either on their own account as merchants or peddlers, of their agricultural produce (Balearic onion sellers are, surprisingly, numerous in

France), or as hired crews and mercenaries—even, in the past, as pirates. There is a considerable Jewish cultural tradition in Majorca, and many nations have fought for possession of the islands, including Britain, which ruled them on and off from 1708 to 1802.

From the Balearic Islands has also come a stream of emigration. Despite the tourist occupation, which has contributed to the growth of the capital, Palma, from 85,000 in 1925 to 165,000 at the present time, restricted opportunities at home have impelled many persons to move to French North Africa and the New World, especially South America.

SHORT BIBLIOGRAPHY

ADAMS, NICHOLSON BARNEY. *The Heritage of Spain: An Introduction to Spanish Civilization.* Rev. ed. New York: Holt, 1959.

ALTAMIRA Y CREVEA, RAFAEL. *A History of Spain, from the Beginnings to the Present Day.* Princeton, N.J.: Van Nostrand, 1949.

BOLÓS Y CAPDEVILA, MARÍA DE. *Enciclopedia geográfica de España.* 2d ed. Barcelona: De Gasso, 1958.

BRENAN, GERALD. *The Face of Spain.* New York: Macmillan, 1943.

———. *The Literature of the Spanish People, from Roman Times to the Present Day.* Cambridge: Cambridge University Press, 1951.

———. *The Spanish Labyrinth.* 2d ed. Chicago: Pellegrini and Cudahy, 1951.

CARCER DE MONTALBAN, ANTONIO DE. *Geografia gráfica de España.* Barcelona: Hymsa, 1934.

CASTRO, AMÉRICO. *The Structure of Spanish History.* Princeton, N.J.: Princeton University Press, 1954.

CHAPMAN, CHARLES EDWARD. *A History of Spain.* New York: Free Press of Glencoe, 1965.

CROW, JOHN A. *Spain, The Root and the Flower: A History of the Civilization of Spain and of the Spanish People.* New York: Harper, 1963.

HÜRLIMANN, MARTIN. *Spain.* New York: Studio Publications, 1954.

INTERNATIONAL BANK FOR RECONSTRUCTION AND DEVELOPMENT. *The Economic Development of Spain.* Baltimore: Johns Hopkins Press, 1963.

KLEIN, JULIUS. *The Mesta: A Study in Spanish Economic History, 1273–1836.* Cambridge, Mass.: Harvard University Press, 1920.

LA SOUCHÈRE, ELENA DE. *An Explanation of Spain.* New York: Random House, 1964.

LIVERMORE, HAROLD. *History of Spain.* New York: Farrar, Straus and Cudahy, 1959.

MADARIAGA, SALVADOR DE. *Spain: A Modern History.* New York: Praeger, 1958.

MATTHEWS, HERBERT L. *The Yoke and the Arrows: A Report on Spain*. Rev. ed. New York: Braziller, 1961.

MEYNAT, JEAN. *La Péninsule ibérique*. Paris: Les Cours de droit, 1957.

MOLINER DE ARÉVALO, MATILDE. *Geografia de España*. Madrid: Compania bibliográfica española, 1955.

MORRIS, JAMES. *The Presence of Spain*. New York: Harcourt Brace & World, 1964.

Nuevo Atlas de España. Madrid: Aguilar, 1961.

OTERO PEDRAYO, RAMÓN (ed.). *Geografia de España*. 4 vols. Barcelona: Instituto Gallach de Libreria y Ediciones, 1955–56.

PETERS, E. A. (ed.). *Spain: A Companion to Spanish Studies*. 5th ed. New York: Pitman, 1957.

PRITCHETT, V. S. *The Spanish Temper*. New York: Knopf, 1954.

SORRE, MAX. *Méditerranée, Péninsules méditerranéenes*. (*Géographie universelle*, Vol. VII.) Paris: Colin, 1934.

THOMAS, HUGH. *The Spanish Civil War*. New York: Harper, 1961.

WAY, RUTH, and SIMMONS, MARGARET. *A Geography of Spain and Portugal*. New York: Dutton, 1962.

WELLES, BENJAMIN. *Spain: The Gentle Anarchy*. New York: Praeger, 1965.

WOLGESINGER, MICHAEL. *Spain: 230 Photographs*. With an Introduction by Margot Schwarz. New York: Praeger, 1957.

INDEX

PLATES

1a The Southern Slopes of the Cantabrian Mountains
1b The Pyrenees, Valle de Espot, Lérida

2 The Sierra de Gredos, Central Spain, in Winter

3a The Meseta near Burgos
3b A Typical Meseta Village north of Valladolid

4 Rice Fields
on the Albu-
fera near
Valencia

5 Los Peares
Hydro-electric
Installation
showing Dam
and Power
Station

6 The Roman Aqueduct, Segovia

7 The Alhambra at Granada showing Arabesque design

8 A Typical Street in Seville